ENVIRONMENTS OUT THERE

by Isaac Asimov

Foreword by Tad Harvey

SBS **SCHOLASTIC BOOK SERVICES**
New York Toronto London Auckland Sydney

3rd printing .... September 1970

Printed in the U.S.A.

CONTENTS

FOREWORD

I FIRST met Isaac Asimov when I was twenty-two, a very inexperienced, very nervous, very ignorant would-be science editor. It was 1957, and I was working for *Science World* magazine, feeling out of my depth most of the time and over-worked—all of the time. Finally, though, the summer came, and we had no more deadlines, no more late nights, no more issues to get out until school started again in September. A delightful feeling, I assure you.

I was sitting at my desk one June morning, doing some research on a subject I had been neglecting (baseball box scores), when the editor-in-chief appeared at my shoulder and said, "I see you're terribly busy, but could you possibly find time to read over this manuscript by Isaac Asimov? We'd like to run it in one of our early fall issues."

"Just read it?"

"That's right, just read it over and give me your ideas tomorrow afternoon."

Aha, I thought, a trap. Obviously, the piece was riddled with errors and sloppy writing, and I was supposed to spot these flaws. I forget exactly what the article was about—I think it was the science of measurement—in any case, it was a complex subject that I knew next to nothing about. Feeling put upon, I went over to the library, read as many of the relevant encyclopedia articles as I could, and then signed out three or four books. That night was a late one.

The next morning I read Isaac Asimov's manuscript.

No, I said to myself. This can't be. It's too easy, too effortless. He must be leaving out things, oversimplifying, falsifying. And the way he writes. Why, he sounds like a veteran explorer telling you an adventure story. Read it again, check those facts.

I spent the rest of the morning and my lunch hour with my books and Isaac Asimov's manuscript, digging for errors. I could find none.

"Well, what did you think of it?"

"Very interesting," I said. (Be careful, I warned myself, it still may be a trap.)

"You think so?"

"I couldn't find anything *wrong* with it."

"Hum. I see. All right. I'll take it back."

Well, there goes my job, I thought.

But I didn't lose my job; and, that fall, I found out why. In October, Isaac Asimov's article appeared in *Science World*. If one word had been changed, I didn't notice it.

It was a dirty trick to play on a young science editor, you'll have to admit. But I've long since forgiven that editor-in-chief. I learned a couple of things I've never forgotten. I learned that *good* science writing is never dull and, when it comes to science writers, Isaac Asimov is very, very good.

The eight chapters in this book originally appeared as a series in *Science World* during the 1963–64 school year. Many new facts have been learned about the planets of the solar system since Dr. Asimov wrote the final installment of "Environments Out There." Thus, the most important discoveries through 1966 have been incorporated in the text.

And that leads to a word of warning. In the years ahead, space probes, manned space voyages, radio astronomy and other techniques developed by the ingenuity of astronomers will tremendously expand and sharpen our view of the heavens. Our present picture of "Environments Out There" may seem, then, to be way out of focus. No great cause for worry, though. If this should happen, Isaac Asimov—college professor, biochemist, science fictioneer, writer, lecturer, educated dreamer—will know all about it and he'll be happy to share his knowledge with us.

TAD HARVEY

1. FIRST STOP IN SPACE

PHASES OF EARTH'S MOON AT 4, 7, 10, 14, 20, 22 AND 26 DAYS

THE MOON IS located in the Earth's neighborhood, only a quarter of a million miles away. It is just as far from the sun as Earth is. Both worlds get just the same quantity of heat and light. Yet, despite these similarities, the moon is not at all like the Earth. Our world is full of life. The moon is dead!

Small World

The chief trouble with the moon as an environment for life is its smallness. Its diameter is only 2,160 miles, about the distance from New York City to Phoenix, Arizona. It has a surface area of 14 million square miles, which is smaller than that of North and South America taken together. It is less than an eightieth as massive as the Earth.

Since the moon is such a small world, its gravitational force is small, too. The moon's gravity is only a sixth that of the Earth.

What a tremendous difference this makes! An atmosphere is held to a planet by the force of gravity. The Earth's gravity is strong enough to hold an atmosphere, but the moon's is not. So, there is no air on the moon.

7

In the absence of air, water turns to vapor and the moon's gravity is not able to hold it. It leaks out into space. So, the moon has no water either.

Silent World

Since life as we know it cannot develop without water, it seems certain that the moon is a dead world. There is a chance that in some out-of-the-way places — in the shadow of crater walls, perhaps — traces of water and air may linger.

In 1969, astronauts landed on the moon and brought back rocks from its surface. These rocks showed no traces of water or life, but of course, there are many other places to explore on the moon. Nor were they able to get samples of rock from several feet below the surface. Meanwhile, astronomers are insisting that any objects sent out to land on the moon be completely sterilized. We don't want to infect the moon's surface with Earthly life before we have discovered whatever native life may exist there.

The absence of air makes for a strange and even dangerous world. Air carries sound, for instance. Without air, the moon is a silent world, and moon explorers will feel as though they were

Ghostly mountain range looms across the silent lunar plain. The rim of an ancient crater, range is 3 miles long and rises 500 feet above the horizon. Soft-landing Surveyor snapped photo.

watching a television screen with the sound turned off—although they will hear each other on radio and will detect vibrations carried through the ground beneath their feet.

Radiation Hazard

Air absorbs and scatters light, and the Earth's atmosphere is a protective blanket against radiation. On the moon, the sun's light blazes down unsoftened by air. It is full of strong ultraviolet and even x-rays. There are electrons and other particles shot out by the sun, and cosmic ray particles from outer space.

Moon explorers will have to guard against this "hard" radiation at all times. They will probably be able to step out into direct sunlight for only a few moments. Even then, their transparent face masks will have to be composed of special substances that will cut out hard radiation.

Meteor Hazard

An atmosphere also serves as protection against meteors. These are rock bodies, ranging from some that weigh dozens of tons to trillions of *micrometeors* that are no bigger than tiny dust particles. Space in the neighborhood of the Earth and moon is full of them.

When headed toward Earth, meteors heat up as they plow through the upper atmosphere. Reason: friction between the meteor and the atmosphere. They melt and glow, and we call them "shooting stars" when we see them. Almost all meteors melt away completely long before they reach the Earth's surface. Only a few of the very largest meteors hit the ground; they are then called *meteorites*.

On the airless moon, all the meteors strike the moon's surface silently and coldly—but with tremendous impact. These may be a danger to the moon explorer. Even a small meteor could puncture a space suit and produce a leak, then hit the man inside, too. Perhaps explorers will have to move about with metal "umbrellas" that will slow up small meteors to the point where they bounce off the space suit instead of penetrating it.

In the youth of the solar system, there were many more meteors, especially large ones, drifting through space. It is believed that these collided with the moon's surface and left circular craters, some more than 100 miles across. There are many thousands of such craters all over the moon's surface, as well as many Earthlike mountain ranges.

To explorers on the moon's surface, however, the craters and mountains won't seem very impressive, for they slope rather gently. Moreover, they will be easy to climb, for an explorer will be much lighter than he would be on the Earth—thanks to the moon's weak gravity. Even a massive space suit won't slow him down much. Climbing a moon peak as high as Mount Everest (29,028 feet) should take scarcely more physical effort than climbing Mount Washington (6,288 feet) on Earth.

"Seas" of the Moon

There are flat spots on the moon, too; some circular plains are more than 500 miles wide. These are called *maria* (meaning "seas" in Latin, because early astronomers thought they were seas). The maria may be the remains of enormous craters that were gouged out long ago by colossal meteors and were then filled up with lavalike material.

A moon explorer standing in the middle of a maria or the interior of one of the large craters might not be aware of the surrounding high crater walls. Why? Since the moon is smaller than the Earth, it curves more sharply and the horizon is nearer. If the explorer were in the center of a crater, the distant crater walls might well be below the nearby horizon. The explorer would see nothing but flatness, broken only by small pits, or "craterlets," made by smallish meteors.

Curiously, the maria and the large craters do not seem to be evenly distributed over the moon. At least, this is the evidence

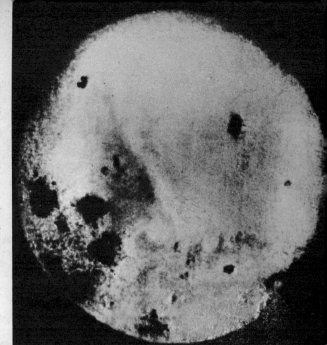

The far side of the moon (*right*) was first revealed to man by the Soviet space probe Lunik III in 1959. In 1966 the U.S. craft Lunar Orbiter made sharp closeups (*below*) of the southern portion of the far side.

from photographs taken by cameras on the Soviet spacecraft Zond 3. On the far side of the moon—the half of the moon we never see from Earth—the Soviet photographs show both fewer maria and fewer large craters. Why should this be? Astronomers aren't sure. "Clearly," says one, "the moon is trying to tell us something."

Mystery Surface

The flat surfaces on the moon may present a special danger. All the meteors striking the moon through billions of years may have pulverized the surface and created a layer of fine dust many feet

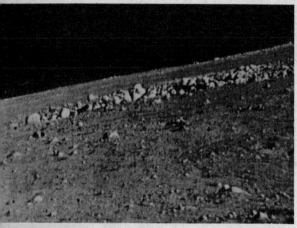

Crunchy, crusty, dusty or rocky? The texture of the moon's surface remains a subject of hot debate. But these photos relayed by Surveyor give the appearance of a firm area able to support men and heavy equipment. Boulder-studded plain at top is several hundred feet across. Closeup (*bottom*) shows fine-grained soil beside footpad of craft.

thick. A careless moon explorer might suddenly sink to his death. So, it may be necessary for him to walk about on broad snowshoe-like boots to prevent this.

But the dust-layer theory is just one of many guesses about the moon's surface. Not even the 11,000 pictures taken by the TV cameras aboard the U.S. moon probes, Ranger 7 and Ranger 8 in 1964 and 1965, provided a final answer concerning the actual structure of the lunar terrain.

After studying the Ranger pictures, one famous astronomer, Dr. Gerard Kuiper, offered this description: "a frothy surface like crunchy snow which could hide many treacherous things." Another scientist, Nobel Prize winner Dr. Harold Urey, holds to the dust-layer theory. The dust could be 60 feet deep in most places, says Dr. Urey; but, possibly, there may be small exposed patches of harder material at the bottom of some craters.

A great guessing game! Could it be that the moon's surface is all these things? Here, like crunchy snow; there, a dust layer; over there, a hard, rocky highland? A Surveyor spacecraft soft-landed its payload of instruments on the moon in 1966 and sent back magnificent information. In its place of landing at least, the soil was pebbly and firm. Is it that way everywhere? The astronauts who walked on the moon in 1969 had no difficulty. They found the surface quite solid though there was some dust on the surface which was disturbed by their engines when they landed and in which they left clear foot-prints.

Land of Never-Gray

Dust or no dust, the "moonscape" will have a weird, forbidding beauty. Since there is no atmosphere to scatter light, the sky above the moon explorer will always be black, never blue or gray.

No light will be scattered into shadows either. On the Earth, where shadows are gray, we can read comfortably in shadow by the scattered light of the sun. On the moon, shadows are pitch black. If a moon explorer steps behind a boulder to get out of the sunlight, he will step into dark midnight—but perhaps not darkest midnight. . . .

Recent studies have indicated that the moon's glow may not all be due to reflected sunlight. Apparently, some spots on the moon are at least slightly *luminescent*—that is, they glow with a light of their own. These areas must contain some kind of luminescent material that emits light when hit by charged particles. The charged particles, of course, are part of the rain of radiation continually pouring out from the sun and are especially abundant when solar flares are at a peak. Perhaps, then, there will be patches and pinpoints of light to cheer the explorer in the darkness of the moon.

View from the Moon

Without scattered light, the stars will always be visible, even when the sun is bright in the sky. The sun may dazzle the moon explorer's eyes, if it is in view, but if he views the sky from a patch of shadow, he will see the stars.

With no atmosphere to make starlight waver, the stars will not twinkle but will shine steadily. Without clouds to obscure them or air to dim them, there will be nearly twice as many stars visible in the moon's sky as in our own, though the additional stars will be very dim. The stars will be arranged, of course, in the same familiar constellations that are visible from the Earth.

To a man standing on the moon, the stars will appear to travel across the sky more slowly than they appear to do to a man on the Earth. Why? Because the moon rotates so slowly. The Earth's pull on the moon is so strong that it has slowed down the speed of the moon's rotation to the point where it has stopped that rotation with respect to us. As a result, the moon always turns the same face toward the Earth as it makes its monthly revolution.

As the moon circles the Earth, however, it presents each part

14

From Earth's moon, the universe looks dark always. Because there is no atmosphere the stars shine constantly; they do not twinkle.

of itself to the sun and to the stars. Thus, the moon has a day and night, each two weeks long. The sun, and each star as well, takes 14 days to go from rising to setting. Without an atmosphere, of course, there is no dawn before sunrise and no twilight after sunset.

Temperature Extremes

With the sun steadily blazing down for two weeks, sunlit areas on the moon will reach a temperature equal to, or above the boiling point of water. After the long two-week night, the same spots may be 200 degrees below zero Fahrenheit. However, these great temperature changes may be confined only to the very surface layer, for the dust and rocks of the moon's surface are poor heat conductors—another way of saying they are good *thermal insulators*. Thus, a few feet below the surface, the temperature may be quite mild, and may stay the same through day and night.

What about the interior of the moon? Up until 1965, it was almost an accepted scientific fact that the moon's interior was cold and hard. Then, Soviet scientists revealed a study hinting that the moon's interior might be radioactive. Furthermore, "hot" radio waves from inside the moon indicated that the core is molten, not solid. If the observations are correct, the Soviet's conclusion makes sense: A high level of radioactivity at the center of the moon would keep the core molten.

Views of the Earth

Since the moon turns only one face to the Earth, the Earth always stays in the same spot in the moon's sky. Because the moon travels in an ellipse and not in a perfect circle, the Earth may seem to wobble just a bit, but hardly enough to be noticeable.

Over about 40 per cent of the moon's surface, the Earth is never visible. This is the far side of the moon that Soviet space probes photographed. Over another 40 per cent of the moon's surface, the Earth is always visible in the sky. Finally, over the remaining 20 per cent, the Earth is located almost at the horizon, and because it seems to wobble, it sometimes dips below the horizon and sometimes rises above it.

The Earth is a glorious sight as seen from the moon. It goes through phases just as the moon does to an Earth observer. But the Earth, when viewed from the moon, will be nearly four times as wide as the moon looks from Earth. The "full Earth" as seen from the moon will have 13 times the surface of the full moon seen by us. What's more, since the Earth's atmosphere reflects far more sunlight than the moon's dull surface, the full Earth will be 80 times brighter than a full moon.

The continents and oceans of the Earth won't be clearly visible from the moon. The Earth's atmosphere will scatter light and form a bluish haze over the Earth, and white clouds will hide about half the globe anyway. Thus, the Earth will be a blue-white globe with ever-changing cloud formations. The swirling spiral of

A crescent Earth hangs over the moon's horizon. This remarkable photo was taken by Lunar Orbiter, reconnaissance craft for a manned landing. Moon explorers will see the Earth go through phases, just as we see moon go through phases from the Earth.

a traveling hurricane or typhoon may be visible at times.

As the sun slowly drifts across the moon's sky, it will usually pass above or below the globe of the Earth. Occasionally, however, it will pass behind the Earth and be eclipsed. On Earth, we see this as a *lunar eclipse*.

Once the sun passes behind the Earth, the observer on the moon will see the atmosphere around the Earth glow orange-red with sunlight. The surface of the moon will turn dull red. The globe of the Earth itself will be black. This might last for more than an hour until the sun again comes peeping out from behind the Earth to turn everything harsh black and white once more.

Walking on the moon will be a tricky task. The gravity is only a sixth that of Earth's and a jump will carry a man 25 feet high. Here an astronaut tries out a space suit on moonlike terrain.

Home on the Moon

Now that men have landed on the moon, we can think about the next step. We may decide to set up a permanent moon colony under the surface. In a sealed underground cavern, air and water can be collected. The solid material of the moon itself, lying between the cavern and the surface, will protect the colonists from radiation, meteors, heat, and cold. One scientist predicted that moon colonists will be able to tap the oxygen locked up in moon rocks. Some 45 lbs. of rock would yield 12 lbs. oxygen. Using this cavern as a base, explorers will venture over the moon's surface.

Within the cavern, it will be almost like home—except for the gravity. A 150-pound man will weigh only 25 pounds. If he jumps, he will soar six times as high and as far as he would on the Earth. At the top of the jump he will be moving quite slowly, but by the time he reaches ground again, he will be moving as quickly as after the same jumping effort on Earth.

With less gravity, moon explorers will also have to contend with less friction because they will be pressing less hard against the floor. This means that everything a moon explorer walks on will seem more slippery than it would on Earth. Surfaces will have to be made particularly rough in order to increase friction, and men and women on the moon may take to wearing specially weighted shoes. Even so, they will have to practice walking and moving under light gravity, if they are not to fall or bump at every step.

The light gravity carries another danger with it. The muscles, working against so much less weight, may grow dangerously flabby. Explorers will probably have to exercise regularly.

If they don't, they may never be able to return to Earth without great physical suffering. For when the moon explorers land once more on the Earth, the open air and blue skies may seem wonderful and the sight of grass and trees and cities like paradise. But unless they have kept fit, they will step from their spaceship and sink to their knees, unable to fight the pull of Earth's gravity.

2. THE INSIDE PLANETS

ORBITING BETWEEN ourselves and the sun, there are two sizable chunks of matter. One of these, the closer one, is almost Earth's twin. Its diameter is 7,700 miles, compared to Earth's 7,927. Its surface gravity is just about seven-eighths that of Earth's—not much different. And it has an atmosphere that might be like Earth's—a thick layer of clouds that never lifts and never breaks. The name of this body? The planet Venus.

If Venus seems very like the Earth, the other sizable chunk of matter appears to be very like the moon. It is a little larger than the moon, with a diameter of about 3,000 miles, versus the moon's 2,160. This body's surface gravity is about twice the moon's, or about a third that of Earth's. Its name: planet Mercury.

Could life develop on these planets? If man got to them, could he survive?

Venus—Veiled Sister

Let's look first at Venus. It is, of course, closer to the sun than the Earth is—only 67 million miles from the sun, compared to our own 93 million miles. This means that Venus gets about twice as much light and heat from the sun as we do. But then its dense cloud layer reflects more, too. Venus reflects 76 per cent of the light that falls upon it, whereas the Earth reflects only 40 per cent.

Just these few facts might lead us to believe that Venus, like Earth, was teeming with life. In fact, back in the 1930's, it was popular to picture Venus as a warm, wet world under eternally gray skies. People imagined it to be like a steamy tropical jungle —perhaps with huge dinosaurlike monsters wandering through grotesque plant growth.

But astronomers were not satisfied, to say the least. In their observatories, they spread out the reflected light from Venus into a kind of rainbow called a *spectrum*. In that spectrum were dark regions, and from the location of these dark regions, astronomers could tell the substance that produced them. Neither oxygen nor

Mariner 2 confirmed suspicion that Venus's atmosphere acts like a blanket, trapping heat beneath it. Cloud temperatures range from −60° to −30°F. Surface reaches a sizzling +800°.

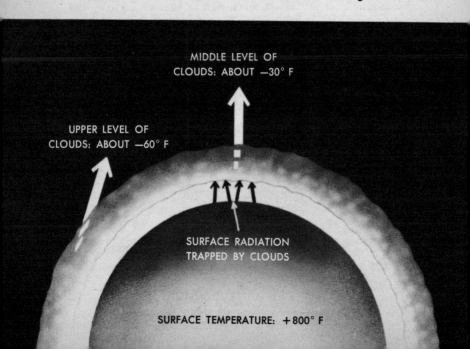

MIDDLE LEVEL OF
CLOUDS: ABOUT −30° F

UPPER LEVEL OF
CLOUDS: ABOUT −60° F

SURFACE RADIATION
TRAPPED BY CLOUDS

SURFACE TEMPERATURE: +800° F

water could be located, but lots of carbon dioxide was found—250 times as much as in Earth's atmosphere.

If there were no water on Venus, the astronomers asked, what made the clouds? Nothing but water seemed to fit all the facts. The trouble was they were studying the light of Venus only after it had shone down through miles of our own atmosphere.

In the 1960's, therefore, several instrument-carrying balloons were sent up to altitudes as high as 20 miles above the Earth, and the spectrum of Venus was studied from there. Sure enough, water—in the form of ice crystals—was detected in the clouds, but no oxygen was found.

The Greenhouse Effect

It became clear to scientists that the great amount of carbon dioxide in Venus's atmosphere might act as a heat trap. Sunlight could pass through it and be absorbed by the planet's surface. The surface could then radiate invisible infrared heat waves. The infrared, however, could not pass through the carbon dioxide and escape back into space. Because of this trapped radiation, Venus would grow quite hot. On Earth a similar process takes place, but on a much smaller scale, because of the tiny amounts of carbon dioxide in our atmosphere. The process is known as the *greenhouse effect*.

Then it was found that Venus was emitting shortwave radio waves of a kind that only a fairly hot body can send out. This made things look even worse. Finally in 1962, Mariner 2 passed within about 20,000 miles of Venus and measured its radio waves. Our worst fears were realized. The temperature of Venus's surface was found to be about 800 degrees Fahrenheit—far above the boiling point of water, far too high for any kind of life as we know it, far too high for man to land on the planet with the kind of equipment we now have.

What's more, whatever water Venus has must all be in the clouds. The surface, too hot for water, is dryer than Earth's driest desert.

23

Reverse Rotation

Mariner 2 by no means gave us the last word on Venus. In 1964, radio astronomers found that Venus rotates on its axis in the "wrong" direction. If you were to stand over the North Pole of Earth, our planet would be rotating counterclockwise beneath you. This has been regarded as the general planetary rule in the solar system. But Venus breaks the rule. It rotates clockwise. Nobody really knows why. The radio astronomers also announced that Venus's speed of rotation was very slow—it takes about 247 Earth days to make one complete rotation about its axis.

Lifting the Veil

Late in 1965, radio astronomy penetrated Venus's thick and ever-present cloud cover to reveal for the first time some of the surface terrain of the planet. Two mighty "mountain ranges" were reported. The first, called the Alpha Mountains, marches more than 2,000 miles north and south and is apparently several hundred miles wide. The other surface feature, the Beta Mountains, appears to be an even bigger range running east and west. As yet, the height of these surface features cannot be determined.

Obviously, much remains to be discovered about Venus. One of the nagging questions: Does the greenhouse effect alone account for Venus's red-hot surface temperature? Or could it be that most of Venus's heat comes from radioactive materials in the crust all over the planet—dark side as well as sun side. If this is the case, nothing man could do would make Venus a safe and comfortable place to live.

Life in the Clouds

Thus Venus, at first glance so like the Earth, turns out to be a horrible, life-forbidding world. But wait—

There is still that cloud layer high in the sky. It is probably cooler than the surface. Could life have developed there? Could microscopic cells float forever among the clouds, carried by an

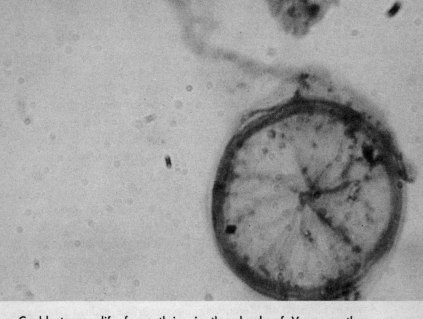

Could strange life forms thrive in the clouds of Venus or the environments of other planets? Maybe so. This Earthly microbe was able to grow in an alien atmosphere of methane and ammonia.

eternal wind? Might such cells extract water from the clouds, draw on the carbon of carbon dioxide, and absorb energy from the sunlight filtering through the very top layer of the clouds?

It doesn't sound likely, but we can't tell for sure until we send some device skimming through the clouds to find out. Some tiny Earth organisms live under conditions just as strange. And the conditions under which life first developed on Earth were hardly less forbidding.

Mercury—Scorched Sister

What about Mercury as a home for life?

Not too promising. Mercury, like the moon, has no atmosphere. And without an atmosphere to protect it from meteors, the planet is probably as riddled with craters as the moon is. Perhaps,

25

think some astronomers, Mercury may actually have been a moon —a satellite of Venus.

Furthermore, since Mercury is the closest planet to the sun, the planet may heat up in spots to more than 750 degrees F., so that it is almost as hot as Venus. In places where the sun shines lower in the heavens, it is cooler, of course. Then, too, there is the sun's deadly ultraviolet radiation to consider. It bombards Mercury's surface in full strength, with little or no atmosphere to absorb it.

About Face

In 1965 Mercury provided a big surprise for astronomers. For many years, they had thought Mercury always kept the same face toward the sun—in the same way that our moon keeps one face toward the Earth as it orbits the Earth. They had always thought the gravitational pull of the sun had slowed down the rotation speed of its tiny neighbor Mercury. But from analysis of radio waves bounced off Mercury's spinning surface, radio astronomers found that Mercury turns more than once in the 88 days it takes to circle the sun. Its period of rotation is either 46 or 59 days. These radio astronomy studies were made at Arecibo Ionospheric Observatory in Puerto Rico.

The discovery explains why temperatures vary so little on Mercury. This has long puzzled scientists. If one side of the planet faced the sun constantly, they wondered, why didn't instruments show that the sun side was much hotter than the dark side? Now they know that both sides experience light and darkness. There are sunrises and sunsets on Mercury, just as on Earth, although they occur at much greater intervals.

Why either a 46-day "day" or a 59-day "day" on Mercury? Can't astronomers be more specific? Not yet, they say. Not after their experience with Venus. Maybe, some say, Mercury rotates backward and clockwise, too. If it does, the period of Mercury's rotation would be 46 days. But if Mercury, like Earth, rotates counterclockwise on its axis, then its complete rotation would take 59 days.

Deadly Sun

In any case, can you imagine the sunrise on Mercury? Huge, hot, and blinding, the sun bursts over the horizon—one of the most awesome spectacles in the solar system. What a pity there is so little chance for man or any living creature to survive that sight!

Yet, at places near the north and south poles of the planet, the sun always stays near the horizon and temperatures may be quite moderate. In these limited areas, Mercury may be no harder to live on than the moon. Of course, Mercury is much farther from us than the moon—at least 200 times farther—and it will be no place for cozy colonies.

Life as We Know It

All right, except for the scant possibility of a few airborne microorganisms on Venus, we've pretty well shattered the idea of

Mercury is small enough to fit into the Atlantic Ocean.

life as we know it on Venus and Mercury. But must life be *as we know it*?

All Earthly life is based on giant molecules—proteins and nucleic acids—dissolved or suspended in a water background. These proteins and nucleic acids are built up mainly of carbon atoms. Attached to these carbon atoms, there are atoms of other elements —chiefly hydrogen, with some oxygen and nitrogen. These giant molecules are stable enough to keep from breaking up, but just unstable enough to undergo the numerous chemical changes that make life possible.

If the temperature is raised even moderately, such molecules become too unstable to keep their structure. Life as we know it becomes impossible.

Different Atoms?

Can we imagine large molecules, complex enough to support life and stable enough to withstand the temperatures of Venus and Mercury? At least we can speculate on the subject. For instance, if fluorine atoms, instead of hydrogen atoms, are attached to carbon atoms, *fluorocarbons* are produced. Chemists have studied these molecules with particular interest during the last 20 years and find they are much more stable than the corresponding *hydrocarbons* on which our form of life is based.

Of course, fluorocarbons are rather inert and don't get involved in many chemical reactions. However, they would react more easily at higher temperatures and besides, chemists have studied only the simplest fluorocarbons so far. More complicated ones might tell another story.

Then, too, the Earth's crust consists of *silicates* which are based on long chains of atoms that are alternately silicon and oxygen. Each silicon atom is attached not only to two neighboring oxygen atoms right and left, but also to two other atoms up and down. In the soil, these two up-and-down atoms are also oxygen, but the chemist can design chains in which these other connections are

$$
\begin{array}{ccc}
\begin{array}{c}
\text{H} \\
| \\
\text{H}-\text{C}-\text{H} \\
| \\
\text{H}
\end{array}
&
\begin{array}{c}
\text{F} \\
| \\
\text{F}-\text{C}-\text{F} \\
| \\
\text{F}
\end{array}
&
\begin{array}{c}
\text{O} \quad\quad \text{O} \\
| \quad\quad | \\
-\text{O}-\text{Si}-\text{O}-\text{Si}-\text{O}- \\
| \quad\quad | \\
\text{O} \quad\quad \text{O}
\end{array}
\\
\text{HYDROCARBON} & \text{FLUOROCARBON} & \text{SILICON-OXYGEN CHAIN}
\end{array}
$$

$$
\begin{array}{cc}
\begin{array}{c}
\text{CH}_3 \quad\quad \text{CH}_3 \\
| \quad\quad | \\
-\text{O}-\text{Si}-\text{O}-\text{Si}-\text{O}- \\
| \quad\quad | \\
\text{CH}_3 \quad\quad \text{CH}_3
\end{array}
&
\begin{array}{c}
\text{CF}_3 \quad\quad \text{CF}_3 \\
| \quad\quad | \\
-\text{O}-\text{Si}-\text{O}-\text{Si}-\text{O}- \\
| \quad\quad | \\
\text{CF}_3 \quad\quad \text{CF}_3
\end{array}
\\
\text{SILICONE} & \text{``FLUOROSILICONE''}
\end{array}
$$

carbon-containing groups. These silicon-oxygen chains with carbon side-chains are called *silicones*. They, too, have been carefully studied and they resist heat much better than do ordinary carbon compounds. The carbon-containing side-chains also hold hydrogen atoms. Perhaps if these hydrogen atoms were replaced by fluorine atoms, the resulting *fluorosilicones* would be even more heat resistant.

New Life?

At high temperatures, is it possible that life might be based on complex silicone or fluorosilicone chains?

To be sure, liquid water is absent on hot planets, and liquid water is necessary to life as we know it. Could some other liquid serve other forms of life? Liquid sulfur, perhaps?

It is hard to tell. There is no way of guessing in advance. We will simply have to go out there and see. In fact, we may find life forms built on so strange a chemistry and possessing such odd and unfamiliar properties, that we will not be able to recognize them as living.

Indeed, interplanetary travel may force our scientists to ask themselves: Just what do we mean by "life" anyway?

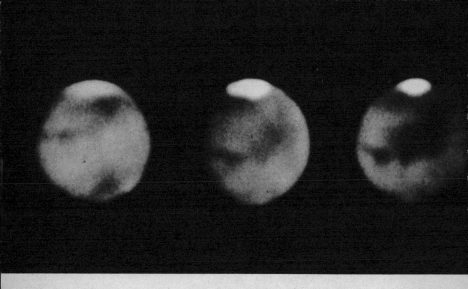

3. MARS AFTER MARINER

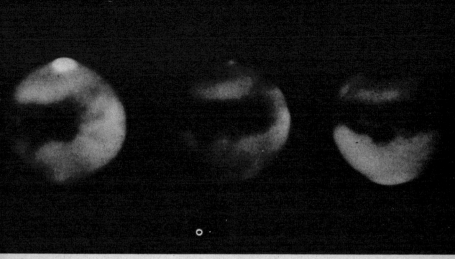

AS SEASONS CHANGE ON MARS, ICE CAPS MELT

THE YEAR 1965 could well go down in the history of science as "the year they tossed a wet blanket over the theory of life on Mars." For that was the year the U.S. spacecraft Mariner 4 took 21 close-up photographs of Mars, from distances of 10,000 miles down to 6,000 miles above the planet's surface.

Discouraging Discoveries

These photographs—as well as a wealth of other information relayed from Mariner's 25-minute flyby—seemed to many scientists to add up to a simple, direct "No" to the dream of Mars as a likely environment for living creatures. Furthermore, new techniques in astronomy, such as radio and infrared astronomy, were coming of age in the mid-1960's and they revealed nothing to brighten Mariner's dismal message.

It looks like our chances of finding even the simplest (one-celled) life on Mars are only slightly better than our chances of finding anything living on the moon. As a matter of fact, after Mariner 4, astronomers started calling Mars "the moonlike planet."

The Case for Mars

What a disappointment! Before 1965, it was possible, based on then existing information, to paint a quite rosy picture of Mars as a life-supporting planet. No other body in the solar system, it seemed, offered such Earthlike conditions. Mars was thought to have a thickish atmosphere, about as dense as the air in Earth's stratosphere. It appeared to have at least some water. It had polar caps that changed with the seasons. It had a temperature that Earthlings would find at least livable, though not always comfortable.

Mars's size, too, looked hopeful. It is a world about halfway in size between the Earth and the moon. The diameter of Mars is about 4,200 miles, about half that of the Earth and twice that of the moon. The mass of Mars (the amount of matter it contains) is about a tenth that of the Earth, but it is eight times that of the moon.

Although the surface gravity of the moon is only about a sixth that of the Earth, the surface gravity of Mars is a little less than two-fifths that of the Earth. If you weigh 120 pounds on Earth, you would weigh about 20 pounds on the moon and about 48 pounds on Mars. So it would be far easier to adjust to Mars's gravity than to the moon's.

With all these encouraging facts, how could Mariner 4 have shattered so rudely the image of a Mars teeming with life?

The Photographs

First, there were the photographs. The Martian surface is pock-marked with craters, large and small. Some of the pictures, in fact, could easily have been confused with the Ranger photos of the moon's surface.

The existence of so many meteor craters indicates that Mars's atmosphere is much thinner than previously thought. Why? Because if the atmosphere were thicker, many of the meteors would have burned up from the friction of Mars's atmosphere before they hit the surface. This is what happens on Earth. Shooting stars are actually meteors burning up in our atmosphere. Meteors are probably even more plentiful in Mars's neighborhood than they are around the Earth and the moon. Mars is right next to the asteroid belt, a stream of rocky debris revolving around the sun. (We'll be looking at those asteroids in the next chapter.)

Scientists now estimate that atmospheric pressure on Mars— that is, the weight of the atmosphere pressing down on the surface —may be only a five-thousandth of what it is on Earth. Such a meager atmosphere would allow most of the sun's ultraviolet radiation to hit the Martian surface—and direct exposure to so much ultraviolet radiation would kill any Earthly life form.

Other Evidence

In addition to the photographs showing the cratered surface, the thinness of the Martian atmosphere was indicated by the fact that the atmosphere had little effect on radio signals beamed through it by Mariner 4. Infrared astronomy also supports the thin-atmosphere finding.

Mariner 4's instruments turned up still another environmental hazard. They found no evidence of any magnetic field around the planet. Earth, on the other hand, is surrounded by a magnetic field, which acts as a shield against the *solar wind*, the high-velocity outflow of charged particles from the sun. Absence of a magnetic field might mean that Mars, unlike Earth, has a solid core, and has therefore not undergone the mighty volcanic and mountain-building forces that have shaped the Earth's surface. Nor did Mariner 4 find around Mars any trace of radiation belts similar to the Earth's Van Allen belts, which hold trapped radiation.

Thus, Mars's surface appears to be a virtually unprotected target for any and all kinds of radiation, not to mention meteors of all sizes. Could life survive this deadly barrage? Obviously, the answer is. . . . But wait.

A Livelier Past?

Has Mars always been such a forbidding place? Some scientists think not. They contend that the Martian craters revealed by Mariner 4 are not nearly so old as the planet itself—only a fraction as old, for example, as the craters on the moon. If the craters are young, then Mars probably once had a denser atmosphere in which meteors burned up. Such an atmosphere would make it likely that Mars also had fairly large bodies of water. Life may have gotten a foothold on the planet before it lost its atmosphere. And some of those life forms may have been able to adapt to the present, almost atmosphereless conditions.

Perhaps, too, Martian organisms may have a kind of "antifreeze" that enables them to survive the planet's cold temperatures. Perhaps their internal fluids contain a large proportion of a kind of salt that prevents their life fluids from freezing. This has been suggested by Dr. Stanley L. Miller, renowned for his experiments on the chemical origin of life. A solution of calcium chloride (a salt) can, for example, be an effective antifreeze down to 65 degrees below zero F. A lithium chloride (salt) solution is even better. It doesn't freeze until the temperature gets down to —100 degrees F. By contrast, a solution of sodium chloride, the principal salt in our bodies, freezes at —4 degrees F.

Dr. Miller, by the way, is one scientist who thinks the Mariner 4 photographs proved "absolutely nothing" about life, or the absence of it, on Mars.

So even after the discouraging news from Mariner 4, the possibility still remains that some kind of life clings to Mars. And there is the fascinating possibility that more complex life forms once existed there.

As for final answers, about all we can do is wait for life-sensing devices to be soft-landed on Mars; and if they don't tell us anything, then we'll just have to wait for astronauts to stride out over the Martian terrain.

Mariner 4 sent home 19 closeup photos of Mars's surface, as outlined on the globe at right. Details of photos 1, 2, 3 and 11 appear below. Astronomers were surprised to find Mars a desolate planet. No signs of life or the elusive canals were detected.

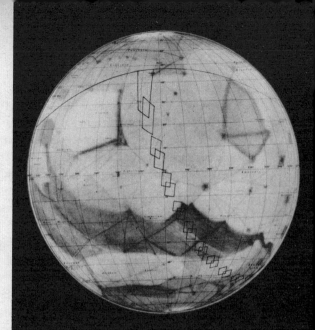

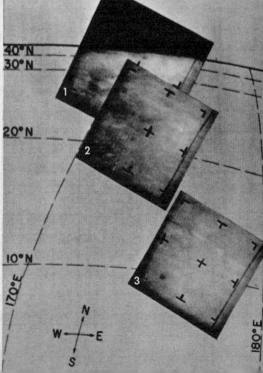

40° N
30° N

20° N

10° N

170° E

180° E

11

1

2

3

N
W — E
S

Deep Purple Sky

Let's take a closer look at what kind of world will greet our man on Mars as he steps from his spaceship.

With only a trace of atmosphere, the Martian sky, even in daytime, will be a very dark purple in color. The threadbare atmosphere cannot hold much dust to scatter sunlight. The stars at night will gleam bright and hard. Even during the day most of the stars will be visible. There will be the ever-present danger of falling meteors.

As he looks out over the Martian landscape, our astronaut will see many craters of all sizes. But he will probably see no big mountain ranges, only some low ridges.

On the whole, our astronaut will find Mars a cold world, considerably colder than the Earth. After all, Mars is farther from the sun, an average of 140 million miles, compared to our average of 93 million miles.

Two-Year Year

Naturally, since Mars is farther from the sun than we are and since its orbiting speed is slower, Mars takes longer to revolve about the sun. The Martian period of revolution is 687 days, or about six weeks short of two Earth years.

About every two years, Mars and the Earth are on the same side of the sun and are said to be in *opposition*. When they are in opposition, the two planets may come as close to each other as 35 million miles. This happens about every 15 years. Mars then comes closer to us than does any other planet except Venus. The last close approach was in 1956. The next will be in 1971—and that is the year the U.S. hopes to soft-land a Voyager spacecraft on Mars.

Incidentally, Mariner 4 brought an end to the idea of using parachutes to soft-land Voyager. In the thin atmosphere, a parachute just wouldn't work; thus a retrorocket brake will have to be used to slow down Voyager's descent.

A Shrunken Sun

Because of Mars's greater distance from the sun, it gets only half as much radiant energy as Earth does. To the astronaut on Mars, the sun will appear shrunken, lighting up the landscape not nearly so well as it does here on Earth.

Because of the thin atmosphere, the daily temperature extremes on Mars are greater than those on the Earth. Despite the great distance from the sun, afternoon temperatures on the Martian equator may be as high as 90 degrees F. Once the sun sets, however, the temperature will drop rapidly, reaching a low of —50 degrees F. by dawn, even at the equator. At the poles, the temperature may reach below —150 degrees F.

These extremes would be even worse if Mars rotated as slowly as the moon, but it does not. The period of Martian rotation is 24 hours and 37 minutes, just about half an hour longer than the Earth's. The extra half-hour will scarcely be noticeable, so that to an astronaut on Mars, day and night will seem normal in length.

The axis about which Mars rotates is tipped with respect to the sun, just as the Earth's axis is tipped, and by almost the same amount. This means that Mars has seasons just as the Earth has. To be sure, each Martian season is colder than the corresponding season on Earth. Also, because the Martian year is twice the Earth year, each Martian season is twice as long as an Earth season.

Airless and Dry

As far as breathing is concerned, the Martian atmosphere is hopeless, of course. Not only is it far too thin to breathe, it apparently contains no oxygen. We have been able to detect carbon dioxide in the Martian atmosphere—in fact, there seems to be more of it on Mars than on Earth.

The best evidence at present suggests that the Martian atmosphere is a mixture of nitrogen (which is very hard to detect), carbon dioxide, and the inert gas argon (also hard to detect).

37

There is very little water on Mars. There are no oceans or lakes or rivers. There is no rainfall. Yet water is not completely absent. Estimates of Mars's water supply range from about as much as is held in our own Lake Erie to "scarcely enough to fill a small pond."

The Polar Caps

But there are the ice caps about each Martian pole. Each ice cap expands during its hemisphere's winter season and contracts during its hemisphere's summer. In fact, Mars's south polar ice cap disappears entirely during the southern hemisphere's summer. The north polar cap never completely disappears. This indicates that summer in Mars's southern hemisphere is warmer than summer in Mars's northern hemisphere. Why should this be? Because the Martian southern hemisphere has its summer when Mars's orbit brings the planet closest to the sun.

The complete disappearance of the south polar cap indicates that neither ice cap can be very thick—a few inches at most—and thus the ice caps do not represent a great amount of locked-up water.

Indeed the latest photographs and other measurements taken of Mars in 1969 make it appear that the icecaps may not be water at all, but frozen carbon dioxide.

Signs of Life

The surface of Mars shows two colors. About three-fifths of it is reddish-orange. Most astronomers think this color is due to iron oxides—to rust, in other words. Sometimes yellowish clouds have been made out in the Martian atmosphere. These suggest that Mars may be swept by high winds and dust storms. The remaining two-fifths of the Martian surface has a darker hue, possibly with a slight greenish tinge. Some astronomers wonder whether that color might not be due to a covering of some form of plant life. Others believe that the dark areas are simply outcroppings of rock, whereas the reddish areas are "dust bowls" composed of pulverized material.

These are Martian canals as drawn by a French astronomer in 1886. Over the years, many reliable observers have reported seeing the canals, but no camera has ever registered them.

The darker areas do, however, appear to change with the seasons. During the Martian summer in one hemisphere, the ice cap about the summer pole dwindles and becomes rimmed by dark areas which may be liquid water soaking into the soil. When that happens, the dark areas expand toward the equator, as if plant life were growing.

It must be admitted, though, that the latest data on Mars — its low temperatures, its thin atmosphere — make the prospects of any form of life rather doubtful.

Mariner 4 revealed nothing about the makeup of these light and dark areas on the Martian surface. In fact, the light and dark markings didn't even show up on the photographs. That isn't surprising, since each photograph covered an area of only 300 square miles, and the outlines of the areas are probably too vague to stand out.

So when the time comes that we can land an object on Mars, we will have to be very careful to sterilize it first. After all, biologists are extremely anxious to study life forms that have developed on another planet. It would be disastrous if we could not tell whether some life form found there was a Martian native or a contaminate from the Earth.

Nobody was really very surprised when no canals showed in Mariner 4's photographs. In 1877, straight lines were observed for the first time on the surface of Mars. Some astronomers suggested that they were canals built by intelligent beings in order to bring water down from the ice caps to irrigate Martian fields.

However, it has always been extremely difficult to reach any agreement on the location of the canals, and most astronomers now believe they are only optical illusions.

Two Tiny Moons

Mars has two satellites, Phobos and Deimos. Phobos is a tiny object, only 10 miles in diameter and only about 3,500 miles

Two miniature moons circle Mars. Deimos (*lower left*) is a mere 5 miles in diameter. Phobos (*upper right*) is 10 miles across.

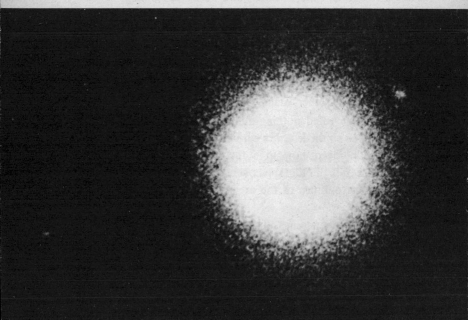

above the Martian surface. Deimos is even smaller, 5 miles in diameter and 12,500 miles above the surface.

Because of its nearness, Phobos will sometimes appear about a third the diameter of our own moon when seen from Mars. Deimos will have the appearance of only a bright star. Phobos revolves about Mars in 7 hours 39 minutes, moving faster than Mars rotates. For this reason, an astronaut standing on the Martian surface could watch Phobos rise in the west, streak across the sky in a little over five hours, and set in the east.

Recent measurements show that Phobos is very slowly drawing nearer to Mars. In a few million years, it will actually crash into the planet. A possible explanation is that Phobos is plowing through the very outer reaches of the Martian atmosphere. Friction with the atmosphere would slow it down very, very gradually, so that it would eventually crash into Mars.

However, Phobos is 3,500 miles from the Martian surface. At that height there is simply not enough atmosphere to slow down an object the size of Phobos quickly enough to account for its spiraling orbit.

A Russian astronomer has therefore suggested that Phobos may be lighter than we think. Instead of solid rock, it may be a hollow shell. What little air is present at that height may then be sufficient to make it spiral inward. But why should Phobos be hollow? Could it have been constructed millions of years ago by intelligent Martians as a space station?

Not very likely.

But it's an exciting suggestion.

In looking over the discouraging news reported by Mariner 4 and other scientific instruments, perhaps we've given the idea that it would be just as well to forget all about Mars as a space destination. Not at all.

Nowhere else in the solar system could men build so comfortable a colony. And nowhere else are there such fascinating puzzles to be solved.

4. MYSTERIOUS ASTEROIDS

ON THE NIGHT OF January 1, 1801, at the very beginning of the nineteenth century, an Italian priest, Father Giuseppe Piazzi made a startling discovery.

Piazzi was a professional astronomer, at work in his observatory in Palermo, Sicily. He had been surveying the heavens systematically for months. Now, on January 1, he came across a "star" that was not supposed to be there. It appeared on none of his star maps. Piazzi marked its position and searched for it again the next night. It was not in the same place. It had moved.

A New Planet

Now, Piazzi was well aware that stars do not move so fast. Planets and comets do, but this "star" was certainly no comet. With mounting excitement, Piazzi watched night after night. Finally, he decided it was definitely a new planet. It was, however, a most puzzling one.

Since it moved faster than Jupiter, it must be a planet closer to the sun than Jupiter. Yet it was too faint to see without a telescope. The only explanation was that the new planet must be small—so small that it did not catch much light. Indeed, this proved to be the case. The new planet was found to be only about 480 miles in diameter. It would take 17 such bodies, side by side, to stretch across the diameter of Earth.

The body was found to move in an orbit between those of Mars and Jupiter. It was about 250 million miles from the sun. It was named Ceres, after the old Roman goddess of agriculture.

Never before had astronomers detected so small a body in the solar system. They could hardly believe that Ceres was the lone occupant of the vast space between Mars and Jupiter. Sure enough, within a few years three more small planets were discovered: Pallas, Vesta, and Juno.

The Asteroids

These bodies were called *asteroids* ("like stars") because when viewed by telescope they did not show up as round disks, as ordinary planets did. Instead, being so small, they appeared only as bright, starlike points. Actually, *planetoids* and *minor planets* are better names, though less popular.

After Piazzi's time, other asteroids were discovered by the swarms—so many that astronomers began to refer laughingly to the asteroids as the "vermin of the skies." At least 2,000 have now been seen, and it is supposed that at least 44,000—perhaps as many as 100,000—exist. Almost all of them circle in orbits between Mars and Jupiter. Most are tiny bodies, not more than a few miles in diameter. No more than 20, perhaps, are larger than 100 miles in diameter, and Ceres, the first discovered, is by far the largest.

Origin of the Asteroids

Where did all these asteroids come from? Many astronomers think that all the planets were formed billions of years ago by the gradual coming together of small bodies called *planetesimals*. Perhaps, in the space between Mars and Jupiter, such plane-

44

Most asteroids are only a few miles across, but some are smaller than Manhattan Island, while others exceed 100 miles in diameter.

tesimals could not get together because of the disturbing gravitational influence of nearby giant Jupiter. In that case, asteroids might be "leftover" planetesimals.

Or perhaps a planet did form and for some reason exploded. Perhaps the asteroids are the fragments of that exploded planet. This is one of the most fascinating mysteries of the solar system.

Colonizing Ceres

Suppose someday we land on one of the asteroids, say, on Ceres. What will it be like? Of course, so small a body does not have gravity strong enough to hold water or air, so it will probably be a bare rocky world, like the moon but much smaller.

By the time we land on Ceres, we will have learned to live on the moon, and a waterless, airless world should hold no terrors. We will burrow under the surface, having brought our water and air with us. Ceres will be cold. But it will be easy to heat an underground cavern. Certainly, with no whistling icy wind, it will not be so cold and uncomfortable as an Antarctic winter.

The sun will be far off. From Ceres, the sun will seem less than a seventh the size it appears to us. The amount of heat and light that reaches each square mile of Ceres is only a sixtieth the amount that reaches each square mile on Earth. This has its advantages: Ceres will never experience the dangerous heat that the moon's surface receives.

What's more, Ceres is not so small as it seems. It may be only 480 miles in diameter, but its surface area is more than 700,000 square miles. This is 20 per cent greater than the area of Alaska, so it leaves plenty of room for exploration.

Ceres' horizon will appear very near. A six-foot astronaut standing on level terrain on Ceres will see the horizon only seven-tenths of a mile away, instead of three miles away as on the Earth. Then, too, Ceres has an extremely weak gravitational force. An astronaut weighing 150 pounds on Earth will weigh only 5 pounds on Ceres. He could easily jump 100 feet into the air; but it will take him 15 seconds to reach the top of that jump, then 15 seconds to come down again. Watch the second hand of a clock for 15 seconds and calculate how long you would be falling. On Earth in that time, a man could fall more than half a mile.

The astronaut will have to get used to such slow rates of falling and will have to practice long and hard to learn to control his own movements. As on the moon, only more so, his muscles and bones may get dangerously soft if he does not undergo special exercises regularly.

Ceres will not be a very comfortable place to live permanently, but it could be very useful as an advance base for the exploration of the outer solar system. Supplies and parts could be brought to Ceres over the years, and a complete rocket base could be established. At certain times, Ceres is only half the distance from Jupiter that Earth ever is. Thus, Ceres would make a good jumping-off place for Jupiter.

Observation Bases

Perhaps Ceres could also be used as a scientific observatory. A close study of Ceres might tell us a great deal about the origin of the asteroids, the makeup of the other planets, and even perhaps about the early history of the solar system.

It might also make a good place for an astronomical observatory. Like the moon, it has no air to absorb starlight. Unlike the moon, no huge blazing sun will interfere with observations.

There is one problem, though. How fast does Ceres turn on its axis? So far we have no idea. We can't see it well enough to spot markings on its surface by means of which we could time the rotation. If the rotation is too fast, it will be difficult to observe the stars—they will seem to whirl by.

Perhaps, someday several asteroids may be occupied by scientific laboratories. One must not, however, think that they will be much company for one another. When you consider that there are 100,000 asteroids between the orbits of Mars and Jupiter, you might suppose that these "vermin of the skies" are so closely crowded together that people on one will be able to wave to people on another.

The trouble is that there is a vast amount of room between the orbits of Mars and Jupiter. Even with 100,000 asteroids, the average distance between them is about 10 million miles. People on Ceres and Vesta will probably never see any other asteroid at all, except with a telescope.

Hitchhiking on Hidalgo

Some asteroids may be useful not only as bases for later exploration, but also as exploring vessels themselves. For instance,

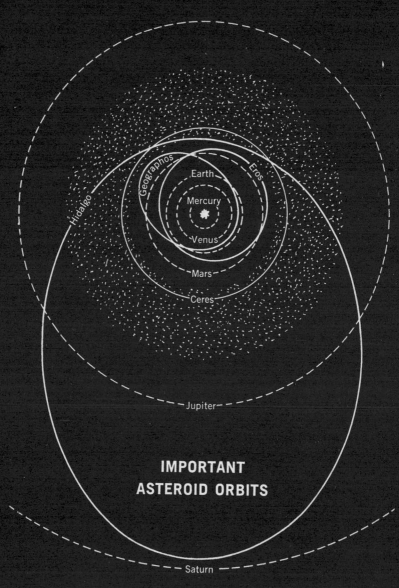

IMPORTANT ASTEROID ORBITS

Countless asteroids swarm the skies between Mars and Jupiter.
Man may someday explore space by hitching rides on asteroids
like Hidalgo and Geographos. These bodies follow elliptical
orbits that take them to distant reaches of our solar system.

there is a curious asteroid called Hidalgo, discovered in 1920. Its very elliptical orbit brings it closer to the sun than Ceres ever comes. At that time, we could reach it more easily than we could reach Ceres. But then, Hidalgo goes looping far out from the sun. It passes beyond the orbit of Jupiter and reaches almost to the orbit of Saturn.

Hidalgo is much larger than any ship we could build and could carry more supplies and instruments. When Hidalgo is in the normal asteroid zone, it could be loaded with quantities of equipment. Then, in the 12 or so years that it takes to make its orbit, the equipment could be set up on Hidalgo, an observatory could be hollowed out, and a vast number of observations of the outer solar system could be made. When Hidalgo returns, more supplies could be landed, as well as a new crew with improved instruments. Eventually, Hidalgo might be used as a jumping-off place for expeditions to Saturn and its moons.

Elliptical Eros

This hitchhiking system would also work on some unusual asteroids that lie within Mars's orbit.

There is asteroid Eros, for instance, discovered in 1898. Its orbit, too, is quite elliptical. At the far end, it travels beyond Mars, out to 200 million miles from the sun. At the near end, it crosses Earth's orbit, nearly to the orbit of Venus. There are times when it is only 14 million miles from the Earth. It is a tiny asteroid, with gravity so weak that Eros is not even squeezed into the shape of a sphere. Instead, it is brick-shaped, about 14 miles long and 4 miles across.

If Eros could be reached while it was passing close to the Earth, enough supplies might be landed to support a colony of astronaut-scientists. In that way, a permanent laboratory could be set up, and the space between Earth and Venus could be explored more safely than in an ordinary ship.

Icarus

The asteroid Icarus, discovered in 1948, is even more remarkable. The far end of its orbit goes beyond Mars, as does Eros' orbit. At the near end, however, Icarus does not merely approach Venus. It crosses Venus' orbit—and Mercury's as well. In fact, Icarus gets to within 17 million miles of the sun. Nothing else ever gets that close to the sun except for an occasional comet.

If an underground cave were hollowed out on Icarus while it was orbiting between Mars and Earth, a colony could survive the close passage to the sun, since rock is an excellent insulator. Special instruments located at the surface would then be able to study the sun.

Asteroid Organisms?

Is there any possibility of native life on the asteroids? In the absence of air and water, complicated life forms like ourselves are not possible. Still, if the asteroids were once part of a planet

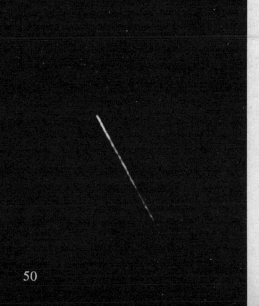

Streaking across the night sky, Eros has its picture taken (*left*). One of Earth's closest asteroid neighbors, Eros may be an oblong chunk of rock (*opposite page*). Sometimes its diameter seems as small as 4 miles, other times as large as 14 miles.

that exploded, perhaps some of the life forms, if any, on the original planet might have survived the explosion.

In 1959, it was discovered that some meteorites contained traces of organic molecules of the kind ordinarily associated with life. Meteorites might also be part of that exploded planet. On the other hand, those compounds might have been formed by slow chemical changes without life being involved.

Then, in 1961, a meteorite was found that contained microscopic objects that might just possibly be the remains of microorganisms.

Were these ordinary objects that just happened to be similar to pieces of tiny organisms? Were they germs that had gotten into the meteorite from the surrounding Earth soil? Or were they really the remains of extraterrestrial life?

We won't know for sure until we can land on some of the asteroids.

Then—just perhaps—we may find out.

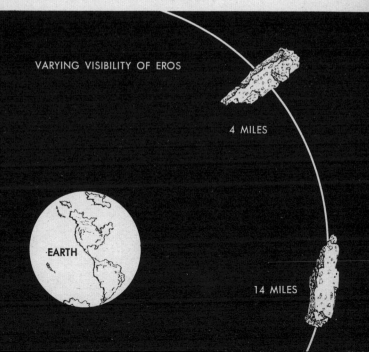

VARYING VISIBILITY OF EROS

4 MILES

EARTH

14 MILES

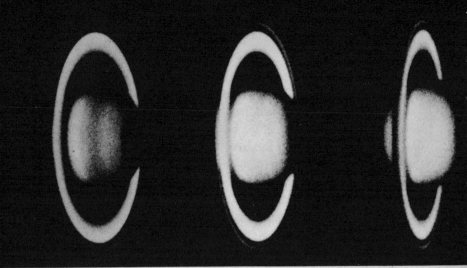

5. THE GIANT PLANETS

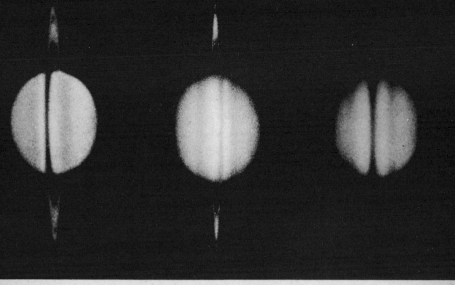

OUT BEYOND the asteroids are the four great worlds of the solar system. Each makes our Earth seem like nothing more than a small round rock.

The largest of all is mighty Jupiter. It is 88,800 miles in diameter at the equator, compared to a puny 7,927 miles for the Earth. It would take eleven globes the size of the Earth, set side by side, to stretch across the width of Jupiter. If Jupiter were a hollow shell, it would take 1,300 planets the size of the Earth to fill it up.

The other three planets don't measure up to Jupiter, but they are giants just the same. Saturn is 75,100 miles across the equator, Uranus is 31,000 miles across, and Neptune is 28,000 miles across.

The Nearest Giant

Of the giants, Jupiter is nearest to Earth. When both planets are on the same side of the sun, Jupiter can be as close to us as 390 million miles. Even then, it is eleven times as far away as Mars is; but Jupiter is so large that it can still be seen quite well through a telescope.

Through the telescope, it is plain that Jupiter is not a true sphere. While its equatorial diameter is 88,800 miles, its diameter from pole to pole is 6,000 miles less—only 82,800 miles.

Why should this be? Well, when astronomers watch markings on Jupiter's surface, they see them disappear and return as the planet makes one complete rotation on its axis. By timing the reappearance of the markings, the astronomers get the exact length of Jupiter's day: Jupiter rotates in 9 hours 50 minutes.

This is a much shorter period of rotation than Earth's 24 hours. Yet, since Jupiter is a larger world, its surface must move through a greater distance to turn completely round its axis. A point on the surface of our equator is carried around at a speed of 1,000 miles per hour. A point on Jupiter's equator moves at a speed of 25,000 miles per hour.

Big Bulge

The rapid turning of a planet tends to throw the material near its equator outward (like clothes in a laundry dryer). Earth's slow rotation is enough to give our world a small equatorial bulge 13 miles high. Jupiter's much faster rotation gives it a bulge 3,000 miles high.

The other giant planets also rotate more quickly—that is, have shorter days—than the Earth. Saturn rotates in 10 hours 14 minutes, Uranus in 10 hours 45 minutes, and Neptune in 15 hours 48 minutes. All the giant planets are therefore flattened at the poles. Indeed, Saturn is even more flattened than Jupiter.

Whirling Gas

There is something odd about Jupiter's rotation. It doesn't rotate all in one piece. At the equator, it turns in 9 hours 50 minutes; but at points removed from the equator, the rotation is slower. Near the poles, the time of rotation is 9 hours 56 minutes. This is not much of a difference, but if we were looking at rock or metal, there would be none at all. We must be looking at gas.

54

Then, too, Jupiter is striped. It has a series of bands running parallel to the equator. These bands are probably the marks of atmospheric storms being whipped about the planet by its rotation. We are not looking at Jupiter's solid surface at all, then, but only at the uppermost layer of its clouds. This is true of the other giant planets, too.

What's more, the clouds must be part of an atmosphere that is very deep. We can tell this by the behavior of the satellites of the giant planets.

Mass of the Giants

Each giant has a number of satellites: Jupiter has twelve, Saturn has nine, Uranus has five, and Neptune has two. From the distance between a satellite and its planet and from the time it takes the satellite to orbit the planet, astronomers can calculate the amount of material in the planet. They can find the planet's *mass*.

It turns out that Jupiter has a mass 317 times greater than that of the Earth. If it were possible to weigh Jupiter on a scale, it would take 317 Earths in the other pan of the scale to balance Jupiter. Jupiter has twice as much mass as all the rest of the planets and satellites of the solar system put together.

Even so, Jupiter's mass is surprisingly low. After all, it takes up 1,300 times more room than the Earth, yet it has only 317 times the mass. The material in Jupiter must be spread out more thinly than the material of the Earth.

If the Earth's material were thoroughly mixed up and a cubic foot of it were taken, that cubic foot of Earth material would weigh 344 pounds. We can say, then, that the *average density* of the Earth is 344 pounds per cubic foot. The average density of Jupiter is only about 81 pounds per cubic foot, so it must be made up of lighter materials than the Earth is. Jupiter must contain a smaller proportion of dense rock and metal than the Earth, and a larger proportion of light gas.

This is true of the other giant planets as well. In fact, Saturn, with a density of only 45 pounds per cubic foot, is even less dense than Jupiter. Each of the giant planets, then, must be covered with an atmosphere that may be thousands of miles deep.

Unpleasant Atmospheres

For many years, no one knew for certain what made up the giant planets' atmospheres. Then, in 1932, the sunlight reflected from Jupiter was analyzed by the astronomer Rupert Wildt. Some of the light was absorbed by material in Jupiter's atmosphere, and from the kind of light that was absorbed, Wildt showed the presence of vapors of ammonia and methane. Ammonia is the vapor with a choking odor you smell in the ammonia water used in cleaning. Methane is a flammable vapor often found in cooking gas. Neither is a pleasant material to breathe. In 1964, hydrogen was observed to be present high up in Jupiter's atmosphere.

Saturn's atmosphere may contain these substances, too. But perhaps Saturn, like distant Uranus and Neptune, is too cold for ammonia to be an atmospheric gas. On Uranus and Neptune, all the ammonia vapor is frozen solid. Methane, however, remains a gas even at Neptune's temperature, and can be detected in that planet's atmosphere.

There are traces of other substances—colorful ones—in the atmospheres of the giant planets. Jupiter's bands are colored cream, yellow, orange, pink, red, and brown. Saturn has paler bands, while Neptune has a greenish tinge. These colors may be due to the presence of molecules called *free radicals*. On Earth free radicals are very unstable and don't last long. But, in the deep cold of the upper atmospheres of the giant planets, free radicals may last for long periods.

All these substances, however, probably make up only a small portion of the giant planets' atmospheres. The major portion, scientists now believe, consists of hydrogen and helium.

The Mysterious Spot

Jupiter's atmosphere, by the way, presents astronomers with a first-class mystery. In one of Jupiter's hemispheres there is a flattened spot that is sometimes a pale pink in color, sometimes a brick red. It is about 30,000 miles across and 10,000 miles from top to bottom, so that it has five times the surface area of all the Earth. It is called the Great Red Spot.

Is the Great Red Spot a gigantic storm that has been raging for years? Is it solid material that has settled out of the atmosphere? No one knows.

How deep are the atmospheres of the giant planets, and what lies beneath them? Wildt thought atmospheric gas might take up most of the room in the outer planets. For instance, Saturn, the least dense of the planets, may have an atmosphere taking up

Like an angry eye, the Great Red Spot glares from the face of Jupiter. What is it—a storm? A sea of heavy matter? Astronomers are not sure. Small dark spot (*upper left*) is Ganymede's shadow.

four-fifths of the volume of the globe we see. For this reason, the outer planets are sometimes called the "gas giants."

Underneath the atmospheres, Wildt thought, lie thick shells of frozen ice; and at the very center of each planet is a ball of rock and metal like the Earth, but larger.

All Hydrogen and Helium

Nowadays, astronomers believe it more likely that the planets are almost all hydrogen and helium. These are the most common materials in the universe. The whole universe is estimated to be 90 per cent hydrogen and 9 per cent helium. The other elements (iron, aluminum, oxygen, and so on) make up less than 1 per cent.

When a planet forms near the sun, the hydrogen and helium are so warm that the light atoms and molecules making up those gases move very quickly. The planets lack the gravitational power to hold them. The hydrogen and helium escape, and planets like Earth and Mars are formed only out of the remaining elements. That is one reason they are so small.

Farther from the sun, the hydrogen and helium are cold and their atoms and molecules are sluggish. The planets hold on to quantities of the gases and grow to be giants like Jupiter and Saturn. The small amounts of other elements present are spread thinly through the two common gases.

As one descends into the atmosphere of the gas giants, the gases are packed down more and more tightly under the pull of gravity and the weight of layers of gas above. Eventually, the hydrogen and helium pack into a kind of solid and actually become like metals.

It may be, then, that the outer planets are made up of central cores containing mostly solid hydrogen and helium plus some rock and ice. These cores are possibly surrounded by thick layers of gaseous hydrogen and helium, with some ammonia, methane, and perhaps nitrogen added.

But that is only a guess. In the mid-1960's, a few astronomers were beginning to suggest that Jupiter and Saturn had liquid interiors, not solid ones.

Far, Frigid Worlds

To add to the unpleasantness of these worlds, they are probably ferociously cold, too. Jupiter is 483 million miles from the sun, and its temperature has been measured as —130 degrees centigrade (—280 degrees F.). This would make Antarctica seem like a summer paradise. The other planets are even colder.

Saturn is 886 million miles from the sun and has a temperature of about —165 degrees C. (—330 degrees F.). Uranus is 1,783 million miles from the sun and has a temperature of about —195 degrees C. (—380 degrees F.). Neptune, at a distance of 2,791 million miles from the sun, has a temperature of about —205 degrees C. (—400 degrees F.).

Can we think of ever landing on such planets? Even if we stayed inside heated spaceships that were strong enough to withstand the mighty pressure of the atmosphere and the force of the gigantic winds, there would be another problem—gravity.

The values given for the surface gravity of the giant planets are not high. The surface gravity of Uranus is 1.0, just what it is on Earth. The surface gravity of Saturn is 1.2, and of Neptune, 1.4. Even giant Jupiter has a surface gravity of only 2.5.

However, these values are for the surface we see—the top of the atmosphere. A spaceship penetrating beneath the atmosphere would sink down to the harder surface of the globe beneath, wherever that is. There the gravity would be much higher. The actual surface gravity, particularly on Jupiter, might well be as much as five or six times as high as that of the Earth.

Even if a spaceship could land safely under such a pull and avoid crashing to dust, could it ever manage to lift free of the planet again? We would need ships with full nuclear power, and lots of it, before we could even consider such a feat.

Dark and Desolate

Could there be life on these outer worlds? Imagine the deep cold, the enormous pressures, the mighty winds, the great gravity, the utter darkness, for light cannot penetrate more than a short distance into those atmospheres. Certainly, there could be no life of the sort we know. We might speculate on a kind of life using liquid ammonia instead of water, but wait—

When we say the temperature of Jupiter is —138 degrees C., we mean the temperature of the upper atmosphere, which is all we see. How about temperatures lower down?

Greenhouse Effect on Jupiter?

Jupiter absorbs sunlight and gives off infrared radiation. However, some of the gases in the atmosphere, particularly ammonia, trap the infrared. The radiation remains in the atmosphere and builds up till the temperature reaches an abnormally high level. This again is the greenhouse effect.

The greenhouse effect may keep Jupiter's temperature at its true ground surface at some comfortable figure, perhaps even above the melting point of ice. There is some actual evidence this might be so, for in 1955 it was found that Jupiter emitted radio waves of a sort that showed its surface might have a higher temperature than had been expected.

Could there, then, be oceans of liquid water on Jupiter? If so, the buoyancy of the ocean water would neutralize the effect of Jupiter's gravity; and under the surface of the oceans, the great storms of the atmosphere would not be felt.

Life on the Giants?

To be sure, Jupiter's atmosphere is poisonous, but a billion years ago, Earth's atmosphere was probably something like Jupiter's atmosphere is now, though not so thick. Life developed in a hydrogen-ammonia atmosphere on Earth; might it not do so on Jupiter?

Dr. Sanford Siegal simulates environments out there under glass. Cacti in foreground survived almost a year in Marslike atmosphere. Microorganisms (in jars) grew in gases poisonous to man and animals. Turtle (in glass dome) lived three months at one-tenth of normal air pressure.

We will probably never find out without actually landing on the planet, alas, but perhaps we can get some better hints if only we move a bit closer. Each of the outer planets possesses satellites that are much easier to land and live upon than the planets themselves.

From those satellites, which we'll explore in the next chapter, we may yet be able to learn more about the giant planets than we can possibly dream of now. Who knows what exciting secrets may be revealed when the spaceships head outward from the asteroid zone toward the gas giants?

6. MOONS OF THE GIANTS

THE GIANT PLANETS of the solar system—Jupiter, Saturn, Uranus, and Neptune—are so hostile in environment that they may never feel the tread of human feet. Each of them, however, can be approached, for each possesses a number of satellites. And beyond the gas giants and their satellites, at the very outer edge of the solar system, is another body—Pluto—the most distant planet we know.

A Wayward Satellite?

Some astronomers suspect Pluto might once have been a satellite of Neptune that was somehow jarred loose and shoved into an orbit of its own. Because of its distance, we have learned very little about it. It is not a huge planet like the four gas giants. Instead, it seems to be a world about the size of Mars.

Pluto's orbit is extremely elliptical. At times, it is as close to the sun as Neptune is, but at other times it recedes to a distance of 4,500 million miles from the sun. At this distance, the sun seems a star only 200 times as bright as our full moon. From end to end, Pluto's orbit is 7,300 million miles wide.

Someday in the far future, mankind may want to establish a foothold on Pluto. From nowhere else will we be able to study so easily the far reaches of outer space. Perhaps we will learn more about the distant cloud of icy asteroids that some astronomers think is the birthplace of our comets.

But before we set up camp on Pluto, we will probably have stations on one or more of the moons of the giants. These satellites, once we reach them, may be no more hostile than our own moon.

Asteroid-Satellites

The planet with the largest number of satellites is giant Jupiter. This is convenient, for it is the nearest and the most interesting of the major planets. We know of an even dozen satellites of Jupiter. The outer seven are tiny worlds, no larger than asteroids.

These are the photos that proved the existence of Pluto. Note how much it has moved in six days. The planet farthest from the sun, it is thought to be too cold to support life.

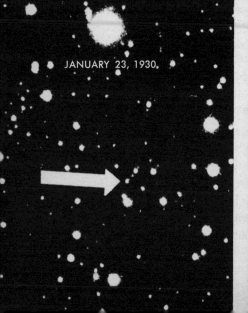

JANUARY 23, 1930.

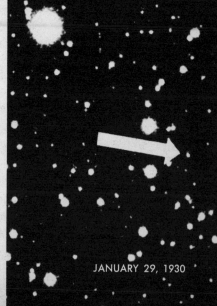

JANUARY 29, 1930

Probably they were once nothing more than that. Since Jupiter circles the sun at the outer edge of the asteroid belt, it is not unlikely that its huge gravitational field might have occasionally trapped an asteroid and made it a satellite.

These seven outer asteroid-satellites have no official names. They are just called Jupiter VI, Jupiter VII, and so on, all the way up to Jupiter XII. The Roman numerals indicate the order in which the satellites were discovered.

The seven outer satellites occur in two groups. First there are the four that circle Jupiter at an average distance of 13 to 15 million miles. These are Jupiter VIII, IX, XI, and XII. All four are about 15 to 20 miles in diameter. All travel in their orbits with *retrograde motion*—a direction opposite to that of Jupiter's other moons. The orbits are elliptical enough to bring them much closer to Jupiter at some times than at others. Jupiter VIII, for instance, approaches Jupiter to within 8 million miles every two years.

Men will find the environment on these satellites like that on any ordinary asteroid, with one exception—they will be a paradise for astronomers. There will be a magnificent view of Jupiter. And the sun will seem a shrunken body—a tiny, pea-sized globe.

Satellite Steppingstones

But men will not linger on the outermost satellites. From Jupiter XII, their ships will move carefully inward. They will land on one of the next set of satellites, Jupiter VI, VII, or X. These circle at an average distance of 7 million miles. The view will be even better than from Jupiter VIII.

Even these will be but temporary camps, for still bigger game lies ahead. Closer to Jupiter is still a third set of satellites: little Amalthea, or Jupiter V, (which is closest of all), and four large satellites. The four are Callisto (IV) at a distance of 1,170,000 miles from Jupiter, Ganymede (III) at a distance of 670,000 miles, Europa (II) at a distance of 420,000 miles, and

Io (I) at a distance of 260,000 miles. These four large satellites were discovered by Galileo in 1619, the first heavenly bodies found with the telescope.

With the possible exceptions of two other satellites—Saturn's Titan and Neptune's Triton—Callisto and Ganymede are the largest satellites in the solar system. Both are at least 3,200 miles in diameter and are not only larger than our moon, but are actually larger than the planet Mercury (diameter 3,000 miles). Callisto and Ganymede are built of light materials, however, so that they are not nearly so massive as Mercury. Io is just about the size of our moon, and Europa is a bit smaller.

Explorers on these large satellites will feel very much as though they were on the moon. The gravity will be about the same and there will be the same airless, waterless conditions.

In one way, the large satellites will be more friendly than our moon. The faraway sun will never bring their temperatures to an uncomfortable point. Nor will shortwave radiation from the sun or bursts of high-energy particles be such a hazard.

A Glorious View

Most of all, though, there will be the view of Jupiter. Imagine a group of explorers based on Io, a world that is almost the twin of our moon and just the same distance (280,000 miles) from its primary planet. At this distance giant Jupiter will look almost 40 times wider than the moon looks to us. It will be 430 times brighter than our full moon.

Yet even that will not be the best possible view of Jupiter. Inside Io's orbit is one more of Jupiter's satellites—Amalthea.

Danger on Amalthea

Tiny Amalthea is only about 100 miles in diameter. What's more, it is terribly close to Jupiter—only 70,000 miles above the top of that planet's mighty atmosphere. Jupiter's gravitational field is strong indeed at that distance and trying to land on the small target of Amalthea will be touch-and-go. Worse yet, Jupiter has giant Van Allen belts, and Amalthea may be dangerously close to these high concentrations of radiation.

Amalthea presents only one face to Jupiter, so to a space camp set up on the side facing Jupiter, the planet will remain motionless in the sky. It will stretch across one quarter of the sky from horizon to horizon, and will appear 2,000 times brighter than our full moon does to us.

Amalthea whips around Jupiter once every 12 hours, in which time Jupiter goes through a complete set of phase changes. When the sun is below the horizon, Jupiter is full or nearly so. As the sun rises, it becomes "half Jupiter" and the planet rapidly narrows to a crescent. Eventually, the sun slips behind Jupiter and remains there an hour and a half. During that interval, there is a "new Jupiter" and only its dark side is visible. As the sun emerges, Jupiter broadens again until it is "half Jupiter" at sunset. It is dark for that hour-and-a-half eclipse every 12 hours.

While these rapid changes are going on, Jupiter's four large satellites form a bright, ever-changing pattern in the sky. In only one other place in the solar system is there a sight more beautiful, as we shall soon see.

Many Moons

Saturn has nine satellites, eight of them medium-sized. Eventually, explorers will move in toward Saturn, using the satellites as steppingstones. The closest of the nine satellites is Mimas— only 85,000 miles from the top of Saturn's atmosphere. Saturn will seem almost as broad from Mimas as Jupiter does from Amalthea. However, Saturn will seem only a fifth as bright as Jupiter, for Saturn is twice as far from the sun as Jupiter is. From Saturn, the sun will be too small to be made out clearly as a globe. Still, it will be nearly 3,000 times brighter than our full moon.

The only really large satellite circling Saturn is Titan, 760,000 miles out. Titan may be even larger than Ganymede and Callisto.

Titan is unusual in that it is the only satellite in the solar system known to have an atmosphere. Bodies smaller than Mars cannot retain an atmosphere unless they are very cold. The cold makes gaseous molecules too sluggish to escape even a weak gravitational field. Even Jupiter's large satellites are too warm to keep an atmosphere, although in 1966 some evidence for very thin atmospheres was advanced. Titan—farther from the sun and therefore colder—could manage.

On Titan, then, the sky may be purplish when the sun is overhead and not pitch black as on an airless world such as our moon. However, we will not be able to breathe Titan's atmosphere. It is probably composed of thin wisps of methane.

Saturn's Rings

From Titan, the chief glory of Saturn will be invisible. Saturn is surrounded by a set of three rings made up of gravel-sized chunks of ice. These chunks may represent matter so close to Saturn that the planet's gravity prevents it from gathering together to form a satellite. The rings circle Saturn's equator, as do eight of Saturn's nine satellites. From any of the eight, even from Mimas, we will see the rings edge-on. So they will be barely visible as fine lines.

Only Saturn's outermost satellite, Phoebe, saves the situation. Its orbit is tilted about 30 degrees to Saturn's equator so that for much of its 18-month circuit about Saturn the rings can be seen broadside. Every nine months they are viewed edge-on and so disappear for a short while. We see the rings broadside from Earth at about the same angle as they are seen from Phoebe, but we must use a telescope to do so. Twice during Saturn's 15-year revolution about the sun, our view of the rings is from the side and so we cannot see them.

Phoebe, unfortunately, is 8 million miles from Saturn, so that to the observer on Phoebe, Saturn will appear only the size that our moon does to us. Also, because of the sun's great distance, Saturn will be only a thirteenth as bright as our moon, even when the planet is full. However, the rings will stretch out on either side—surely, the most beautiful naked-eye sight in the solar system.

More Moons

The planet Uranus has five small moons, the largest only 1,000 miles in diameter. Neptune has two satellites; one of them, Triton, is about the size of Titan and could conceivably have a thin atmosphere.

From the satellites of Uranus, the sun will seem merely an exceedingly bright star—only 1,400 times brighter than our full moon. From the satellites of Neptune, the sun will be only 600 times brighter than our full moon.

From the outer satellites, interesting observations could be made of the stars. We can tell the distance of the nearer stars by their *parallax;* that is, by their apparent shift in position as a planet goes from one end of its orbit to the other. Earth's orbit is only 186 million miles wide. Thus, even the nearest stars are so distant that they shift only slightly as a result of Earth's change in position.

New Star Kingdoms

The satellites of Jupiter move a total of 970 million miles as Jupiter travels from one end of its orbit to the other; the satellites of Saturn move 1,700 million miles; those of Uranus, 3,600 million miles; those of Neptune, 5,600 million miles.

From the Neptunian system, the distances of the stars can be determined by parallax to a depth in space 30 times greater than

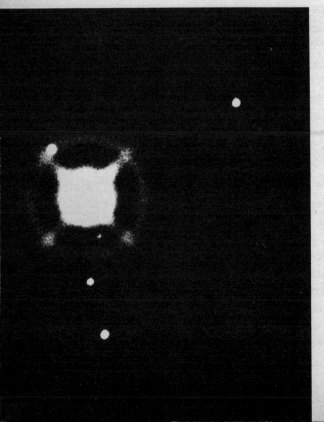

Uranus (left) has five moons. From top to bottom, they are Oberon, Ariel, Umbriel, Miranda and Titania. Neptune (*opposite page*) has two moons: Titan, seen emerging beneath the planet, and Nereid (*arrow*). These moons may someday support bases from which to observe the fringes of our galaxy.

that to which they can be determined here on Earth. This means that the distances of 27,000 times more stars (30 x 30 x 30) can be measured from the vicinity of Neptune than can be measured from the Earth.

But Pluto holds the record in this respect. The distances of three-and-a-half times as many stars can be measured from Pluto as from Neptune. Of course, one would have to have patience. Pluto takes 124 years to move from one end of its orbit to the other, compared to half a year for Earth, six years for Jupiter, 15 years for Saturn, 42 years for Uranus, and 82 years for Neptune.

Then, too, beyond Pluto are the stars—and someday we will be reaching out for them.

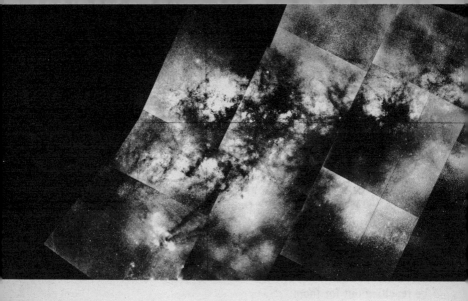

7. THE SEARCH FOR OTHER PLANETS

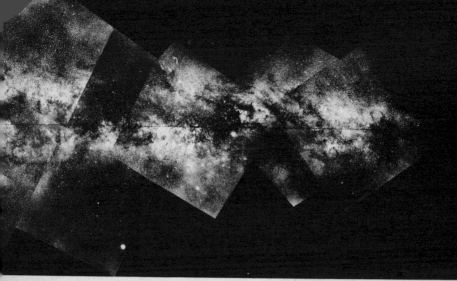

MOSAIC OF THE MILKY WAY—OUR HOME GALAXY

NOWHERE in the solar system can mankind find a planet "just like home." On no other planet but Earth are there a comfortable gravity, a breathable atmosphere, and a sufficient supply of water. There may be life on one or more of the other eight planets, but only primitive life at best. On every one of them, man could live only underground or under domes.

Best Possible Worlds

What we really want is a planet like Earth itself. We want a planet on which weary space travelers could find smiling skies, warm fresh air, good soil, oceans of water. For such worlds we must look beyond our solar system.

What are the chances that such Earthlike worlds might be circling other stars?

Actually, we can only guess. Still, when astronomers make their guesses, based on the best knowledge they have, some very surprising answers turn up. We can follow their reasoning by asking a few questions and giving the most reasonable answers.

Question 1: How many stars are there?

As far as astronomers can tell, their number is infinite. To the very limit that telescopes can reach, there are stars and more stars with no sign of an end. These stars are grouped into huge collections called *galaxies*. Our own star, the sun, is a member of such a galaxy. We see parts of our own galaxy as the Milky Way, so that we can call it the Milky Way galaxy. If we decide to keep to our own Milky Way galaxy, we find that it contains something like 135 billion stars.

Question 2: How many of these stars would make a suitable sun?

Actually, it would be best if the star had about the same mass as our own sun. The more massive a star, the quicker it uses up its hydrogen fuel. Once the hydrogen starts running low, the star starts expanding to a *red giant*, destroying any planets it may have. If a star were more than one-and-a-half times as massive as the sun, it would last less than three billion years before starting to change. It takes longer than three billion years for a planet to develop as the Earth did. In fact, the Earth was probably some four billion years old before it became capable of bearing multi-cellular life.

On the other hand, a star less than three-fourths as massive as the sun would be so small and dim that only planets quite close to it could gather enough heat to be comfortable. If a planet were too close to even a small star, the star's gravity might slow the planet's rotation. One side of the planet would always face the star; and that would make the planet very uncomfortable.

For stars having Earthlike planets, then, we should count only on stars between three-fourths and one-and-a-half times the mass of our sun. Only about one star in eight seems to be in this mass range. Even so, this leaves about 17 billion stars in the correct mass range in the Milky Way alone.

Questions 3: How many stars of the proper mass have planetary systems?

In the first part of the 20th century, most astronomers sus-

Big ear on the universe, the radio telescope at Arecibo, Puerto Rico, is tuned in to deep space. The dish discovered Mercury's 46-or-59-day "day" and Venus's counterclockwise rotation. Do you think it will ever detect intelligent signals from out there?

pected that the solar system originated after an intruding star passed very close by, or perhaps even hit, our sun. As the intruder neared and passed, its gravitational force drew great quantities of matter from the sun and the sun drew equal quantities from the intruder. Some of the matter fell back, but some matter, it was thought, remained to circle the sun and the intruder. This matter, so the theory went, later cooled down to form planets.

According to this theory, planetary systems are rare indeed. The stars are separated by such vast distances that the chances of two stars coming together in a collision are extremely small. Our own sun and the intruding star might well be the only stars in all the Milky Way that had planets.

However, the flaws in this picture soon emerged. As more was learned about stars, it was discovered that most are much hotter in their interiors than has been suspected. Any matter dragged out of stars eons ago was probably too hot to collect into planets. It just puffed away. There were other difficulties with the theory, too.

Then, in the 1940's, a German astronomer, C. F. von Weizsäcker, suggested that a star slowly forms out of huge swirls of dust and gas. As it does so, separate swirls or eddies start in the outer regions of the dust and gas. Result: Small cold planets are formed out of the leftover material. Meanwhile, a large hot star forms at the center. Most astronomers now think that a process like this probably takes place when any star is born, though they disagree on the details.

If Weizsäcker's theory is correct, then practically every star must have planets. Recent discoveries make this seem likely.

Wobbling Stars

A planet circles a star because it is held by the star's gravitational pull. But the planet's gravitation pulls at the star, too. As the planet revolves about the star, the star itself is pulled by the weaker gravity of the planet. The star wobbles slightly.

Astronomers have been seeking such wobbles among some of the stars closest to the Earth. In three cases, wobbles have been detected. From the size of the wobble, they can calculate how large the planet must be. In 1948, a wobble was found in a double star called 61 Cygni. It was decided that a third body, 61 Cygni C, was present. This body is small enough to be a planet but pretty large as planets go. It is apparently about eight times as massive as Jupiter, the largest planet of our solar system.

In 1960, it was found that another star, Lalande 21185, wobbled—and also had a planet that was eight times as large as Jupiter. Finally, in 1963, a wobble indicating a planet only one-and-a-half times the mass of Jupiter was located in connection with a dim star called Barnard's Star.

Barnard's Star is the second nearest star to the Earth, and Lalande 21185 is third nearest. While 61 Cygni is a bit farther, it is still the eleventh nearest. It can't be mere coincidence that three of our nearest star neighbors all wobble, and all apparently have at least one planet. It must mean that planets are common. Astronomers can't help feeling that if we had methods for detecting smaller planets and not just super-giants, we would find that almost every star had a whole set of planets, some large and some small.

Therefore, we conclude that there are about 17 billion sets of planets circling stars of the proper mass in the Milky Way alone.

Question 4: How many stars of the proper mass have Earth-like planets circling them?

After all just any planet won't do. It would be of no use to man if a planet were so large its gravity could crush us, or so small it

Barnard's star (*arrows*) is shifted by the gravitational attraction of an unseen companion—a planet about the size of Jupiter.

AUGUST 24, 1894

MAY 30, 1916

couldn't hold an atmosphere that was breathable. Nor would it help us if a planet were too hot or too cold; or if it rotated so slowly that is was both too hot during the day and too cold during the night. We want a planet that is just right.

Ideal Planets

The chances of a planet having ideal conditions are hard to determine. We know only our own planetary system and it is hard to judge from this one example.

In 1964, an American scientist, Stephen H. Dole, published a book entitled *Habitable Planets for Man.* In his book, Dr. Dole tries to make reasonable judgments based on what we know about the planets of our own solar system. What are the chances, he asks, that a planet circling a sunlike star is at the right distance to be an Earthlike planet? What are the chances that it is the right size, has the right speed of rotation, the right tipping of the axis?

Weighing all the facts as best he can, Dr. Dole concludes that perhaps one planetary system out of every 27 belonging to a suitable star will include an Earthlike planet. This means that in our Milky Way galaxy there may be as many as 600 million Earthlike planets.

Question 5: How many Earthlike planets have developed life?

In the last 15 years, scientists have been experimenting with chemical systems which, they think, resemble those that existed on Earth before life developed. They have found that, under these primitive Earth conditions, the simple building blocks of important substances of living tissue quickly form. They suspect, therefore, that any Earthlike planet will develop life—without fail!

And so in our own Milky Way galaxy there may be 600 million life-bearing Earthlike planets.

Question 6: How many Earthlike planets have developed intelligent life forms?

There we are completely stumped. On Earth, it took at least two billion years of life before creatures as intelligent as man or

Are you looking at other worlds? Calculations show there may be 600 million life-bearing planets in the Milky Way alone.

the dolphin developed. It may be, then, that the development of intelligence is a very rare thing.

Anybody Out There?

Still, suppose that since the origin of the Milky Way galaxy, only one life-bearing planet in 10,000 has managed to develop an intelligent form of life. Even so, that would mean that no less than 60,000 different intelligent life forms existed in our Milky Way galaxy. And, of course, there would be hundreds of millions of different intelligent life forms in the universe as a whole, if all the other galaxies were considered.

That leaves only one more question—

Question 7: How many Earthlike planets are close to us?

That is easy to answer. None!

The nearest stars to Earth are those of the Alpha Centauri system and they are 4.3 light-years away. That comes to a distance of 25 trillion miles. These stars are 6,000 times farther away than Pluto, the farthest-out planet of our own solar system.

How can man ever travel over so huge a distance? And even if he could, how could he reach beyond that to stars 10 light-years away? 100 light-years away? 1,000 light-years away? Our own Milky Way galaxy is, after all, about 100,000 light-years across, from end to end. And beyond lie the other galaxies.

Nearby Earths

But just suppose we do manage to learn how to span the spaces between the stars. Is there a chance that some Earthlike planet may be orbiting one of the nearer stars?

Well, Dr. Dole estimates that within 100 light-years of the solar system there may be as many as 50 Earthlike worlds. He points out that a few of our nearest neighbors among the stars are sunlike in nature and may possess Earthlike planets. He finds there are 14 stars within 22 light-years of the solar system that seem to have the qualities necessary for an Earthlike planet.

The double-star system 61 Cygni is a "wobbler." The distance between the two stars varies because of a third, planetlike body. 70 Ophiuchi wobbles too, but a planet has not yet been detected.

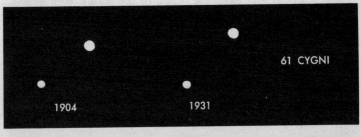

61 CYGNI

1904   1931

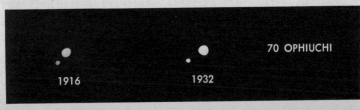

70 OPHIUCHI

1916   1932

Of these 14 stars, the best chance happens to belong, by a stroke of good fortune, to the very stars that lie nearest to us, the Alpha Centauri system. This system consists of three stars. Two of them, Alpha Centauri A and Alpha Centauri B, are much like the sun. In fact, Alpha Centauri A, the brighter of the two, is practically a twin of the sun. Alpha Centauri B is a bit smaller. The two circle each other at distances varying from 1 billion to 3 billion miles, and Dr. Dole thinks that one or both of these stars might have an Earthlike planet. He estimates that the chances are 1 in 10 that at least one of the two has such a planet. The third member of the system, Alpha Centauri C, is a dim, tiny *red dwarf*, far from the other two. Right now, it is a little closer to us than are the other stars of the system, so that Alpha Centauri C is called Proxima Centauri.

The remaining 12 stars that offer reasonable chances for Earthlike planets are Epsilon Eridani, Tau Ceti, 70 Ophiuchi A, Eta Cassiopeiae A, Sigma Draconis, 36 Ophiuchi B, HR 7703 A, Delta Pavonis, 82 Eridani, Beta Hydri, and HR 8832. Considering all 14 stars together, Dr. Dole estimates that the chances are 2 in 5 that at least one of them possesses an Earthlike planet.

Well, it could be worse. We don't have to feel that we must wander among the stars forever on just the faintest of hopes. There might be an almost 50-50 chance that an Earthlike planet is practically in our backyard, as astronomical distances go.

Wild Fancy

But we are only guessing, really. If we are ever to make certain whether there are Earthlike planets among our starry neighbors, there is only one thing to do. We'll have to go there and see. Unfortunately, the ability to travel from one star to the next is as yet only a wild fancy in the minds of a few dreamers.

But then—it was only a few years ago that the thought of men orbiting the Earth and returning safely was only a wild fancy in the minds of a few dreamers.

8. AT HOME IN SPACE

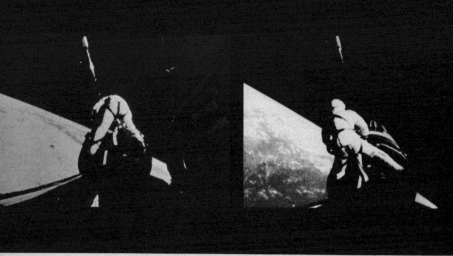

GEMINI COWBOY LASSOES A ROCKET

EVEN THE NEAREST world upon which man can hope to land is separated from us by vast distances of space. We will have to travel some 250,000 miles to the moon, 35 million miles to Mars, 25 trillion miles to the nearest star beyond the sun.

To explore other worlds, spacemen will have to be prepared to spend days, weeks—even years—in space. We must ask: What kind of an environment is offered by space itself?

Earth—Ideal Spaceship

If we think about it, we already live in space. The Earth itself is a huge spaceship that has been traveling through space for billions of years. Man and all other living creatures cling to its surface, held there by the force of gravity.

The only thing that separates us from the vacuum of space is a thin layer of gases, also held by Earth's gravity. These gases form our atmosphere.

We can live on our huge spherical spaceship because Earth's surface provides us with food and water, while Earth's atmosphere provides us with oxygen. The atmosphere also burns up the countless billions of micrometeors that come flying in our direction. It absorbs the energetic radiation from the sun and elsewhere —radiation such as cosmic rays and flying electrons.

If man is to live for a period of time in a tiny artificial spaceship, that spaceship must supply him with the same necessities that Earth supplies. And the spaceship must protect him as the Earth's atmosphere protects him.

Experiments with rockets and satellites have shown us that dustlike micrometeors are not a great problem. They can be warded off by the walls of the spaceship or by a thin bumper layer of metal surrounding the actual walls.

Particle Problems

But sizable chunks of matter, as large as pebbles or gravel, traveling at the ordinary speed of objects in space (up to 20 miles per second) will puncture the walls. Fortunately, these larger particles are very rare. And even if one did hit the ship, the puncture could probably be patched in time.

Much more serious is the subatomic radiation present in space. Cosmic rays and other particles can penetrate the metal walls of a spaceship much more easily than they can penetrate the hundreds of miles of our atmosphere. Some of this radiation is so penetrating that it can go right through ordinary walls. The only way out seems to be to avoid the radiation of space. How?

Our first problem is to avoid the *Van Allen belts*. These consist of high-energy particles trapped by Earth's magnetic field. They surround our planet, at the equator, like two vast doughnuts. It might well be fatal for space travelers to try to push directly through the Van Allen belts. Fortunately, the polar regions of the Earth are relatively free from radiation. So when ships shoot upward to the moon, they will probably follow routes that carry them through the polar "holes in the doughnut."

Even then, there will be hazards. Every once in a while, a great flare of glowing matter erupts from the sun's surface. Vast floods of energetic particles and radiation shoot out for hundreds of millions of miles. This is perhaps the greatest danger of all. Scientists must find out what steps to take to keep our astronauts from dying of radiation sickness.

If we can manage to reach the moon in safety, the worst may be over. The farther outward we go from the sun the less the danger from radiation. To be sure, we must not approach too close to Jupiter and Saturn, for scientists suspect they may have huge Van Allen belts.

Suppose, then, that we are out in deep space, well away from the sun. What other dangers will men have to face?

Weightlessness Worries

There's no gravity in a coasting spaceship—this raises the problem of weightlessness. American astronauts have been weightless

Lethal belts of high-energy radiation surround the Earth. Space travelers can avoid them by escaping through polar "hatchways."

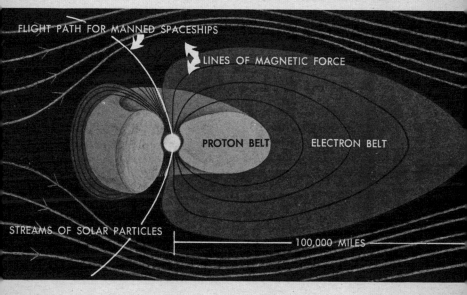

FLIGHT PATH FOR MANNED SPACESHIPS

LINES OF MAGNETIC FORCE

PROTON BELT   ELECTRON BELT

STREAMS OF SOLAR PARTICLES

100,000 MILES

Our home in space as seen from Gemini 11, 850 miles up. Light area to right of antenna is Indian Ocean, dark mass is Australia.

in space for two weeks, and some of the Soviet cosmonauts have been weightless for several days. Apparently, none of them has been seriously harmed, although some of the returning astronauts seem to be prone to a disorder of the canals of the inner ear, called "canal sickness." This causes occasional feelings of seasickness and sometimes a failure of the sense of balance. Whether or not weightlessness is the cause of canal sickness is not known.

Nevertheless, weightlessness for weeks or months is likely to weaken the muscles, soften the bones, and make it very hard for an astronaut to return to the hard grasp of gravity.

One possible remedy is to set a spaceship rotating rapidly. Once such a rotation is started by rocket action, it will continue without any further push. Astronauts inside the ship will be unaware of the rotation, just as we are unaware of Earth's rotation.

The effects of orbital motion will push objects, including the astronauts, against the outer walls of the rotating ship. The sensations of gravity will be duplicated.

Temperature Troubles

What about heat? You sometimes hear people speak of the "icy cold" of space. Actually, space has no temperature. Only matter can be hot or cold. The temperature of small chunks of matter in space depends on their surface and their nearness to a source of heat, such as the sun. Spaceships near the Earth would get so much heat from the sun that the problem would become one of cooling. We don't have to warm our astronauts as they circle the Earth; we have to air-condition them.

Far away from the sun, we will need some sort of furnace on the ship. Heat is lost very slowly through a vacuum, however, so that any heat formed on the ship will stay there. For that reason, the furnace won't have to work hard. It will be far easier to warm a ship in deep space than to warm a farmhouse in a New England winter.

Sustenance in Space

On short space trips, we can carry food, water, oxygen. Concentrated food has already been compounded for spacemen. This consists of syrupy mixtures of fat, carbohydrates, protein, vitamins, and minerals, packaged in crisp dry boxes made of edible cereal. An astronaut can get along very well for one day on a balanced diet made up of no more than 90 ounces of water and 20 ounces of dry food. Add to this about 40 ounces of oxygen. The total quantity of supplies for keeping the human machine going, then, is 150 ounces or, roughly, 9½ pounds per day.

If it takes three days' travel to reach the moon, a week to explore it, and three days to return, there will have to be a total of a little more than 120 pounds of food, water, and oxygen for each man on the ship.

This can be done—but suppose we want to reach Mars instead? To reach Mars, explore it, and return might take a total of two and a half years. Each man on the trip would have to be supplied with five *tons* of food, water, and oxygen.

Does this mean that it is impractical to expect to explore outward any farther than the moon? Not at all! Let's think of our Earth spaceship again.

Cycles for Life

On Earth, hundreds of billions of living organisms are constantly eating and drinking, yet food and water never run out. We are constantly breathing, yet the quantity of oxygen in the air never grows smaller.

The answer to this seeming puzzle is that there are *cycles* on Earth; that is, the necessary materials are built up just as fast as

Space-food garden is a tangle of tubing. Tiny algae thrive on carbon dioxide and other human wastes, produce oxygen and food.

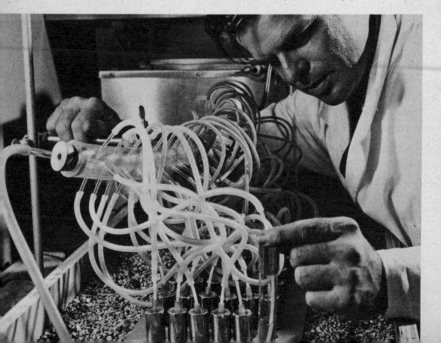

they are used up. Animals consume food and combine it with oxygen to form carbon dioxide and water. However, plants use the energy of the sun to combine the carbon dioxide and water to form food and oxygen again. Fresh water drains off the land into the ocean, but the sun evaporates ocean water and returns fresh water to the land by way of rain.

Food, water, and oxygen have all been kept in continuous supply over many millions of years by the use of energy from the sun. On a spaceship, the same thing will have to be done. Cycles must be established.

Water vapor in the spaceship's air, arising from perspiration and from the breath, can be frozen out by passing the circulating air over refrigerated pipes. The ice can be mixed with the urine of the astronauts. When the mixture is carefully heated, waste products are left behind and the water vapor given off can be collected, allowed to liquefy, and then used for drinking water. This may sound unpleasant, but it is exactly what happens on Earth.

The carbon dioxide exhaled by the crew can be absorbed by chemicals, such as calcium oxide. To restore the oxygen, we can utilize microscopic green plants such as algae. These can be grown in tanks exposed to light, while carbon dioxide from the calcium-oxide collecting tubes is bubbled through them. The algae will also require nitrogen compounds which can come from the liquid and solid wastes produced by the astronauts.

Under such conditions algae grow very quickly (this has been proved in the laboratory). The carbon dioxide is used up and oxygen pours into the air. The wastes are used up and carbohydrates, fat, and protein are formed. As the algae grow, some can be skimmed off or otherwise collected and used as a nourishing food. Experiments are now being conducted on methods for making algae tasty and pleasant to eat.

In this way, food, water, and oxygen will never be used up. Some scientists have calculated that perhaps 1,000 pounds of algae and equipment could take care of the needs of one man indefinitely. This means that only half a ton per man, rather than five tons, would be required for a trip to Mars and back. Furthermore, that one-half ton per man would do for longer trips as well.

Of course, much energy would be required: energy for refrigeration and for heating, energy for light for the algae, energy for the pumping of carbon dioxide, and so on. If a ship were in the neighborhood of the sun or another star, the energy of radiation could be used to charge solar batteries. Out in deep space, nuclear power might be used.

Comfortable Colonies

Imagine a large spaceship carrying hundreds of men and women, rotating to produce gravitational effects, with nuclear fusion power for light and warmth and for all sorts of devices, with libraries and gymnasiums, with elaborate algae systems supplying food and air always. Such a spaceship would be a little planet in itself.

It might be so comfortable on board such a ship that the men and women living on it might be perfectly happy. Perhaps, they would see no reason to land on real planets at all.

But is all this possible? Do you think human beings would be willing to leave the pleasant, warm Earth, the blue skies and mighty sea, the fresh air and beautiful scenery of our planet? Would they want to condemn themselves to a tiny metal bubble of air for years upon years—perhaps for a lifetime? Would they want their children born on such a ship, to live and die there?

I think very few human beings would be willing to do this—at least, human beings used to a planet like the Earth.

But what if human colonies were established on the moon someday, or on Mars? The colonists would have to live underground. They would have to live in bubbles of air, just as they would on a spaceship, except instead of thin metal walls, they would have rock walls.

For colonists on the moon and on Mars, it might not be so hard

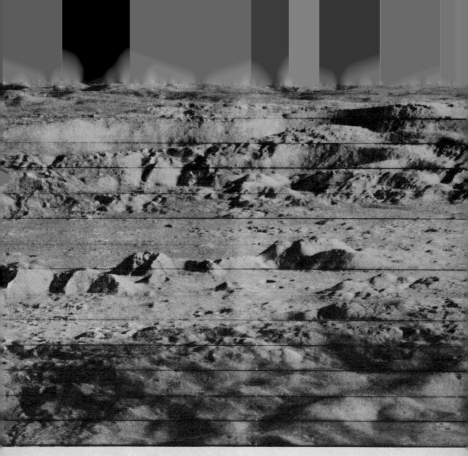

Homesite for the year 2000? Will human beings someday leave the green Earth to settle on the moon or elsewhere in the universe?

to switch from planet to spaceship. They would hardly be able to tell the difference.

Might the day come, then, when much of mankind will declare its independence from all planets? Will countless ships carrying countless human beings someday fill the spaces of our galaxy, slowly making their way among all the billions of planetary systems?

Man will then no longer be bound to the Earth or to any planet. He will be at home in space.

THE END

THE SOLAR
SYSTEM:
A VIEW

H. K. WIMMER

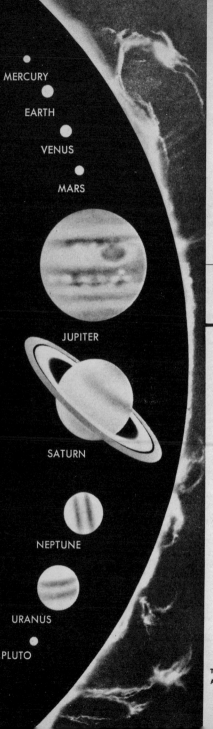

MERCURY

EARTH

VENUS

MARS

JUPITER

SATURN

NEPTUNE

URANUS

PLUTO

THE SOLAF

	MEAN DISTANCE FROM SUN IN MILLIONS OF MILES	PERIOD OF ORBIT IN EARTH UNITS
Mercury	36	88 days
Venus	67	225 days
Earth	93	1 year
Mars	141.5	687 days
Jupiter	483	11.9 years
Saturn	886	29.5 years
Uranus	1,783	84 years
Neptune	2,797	165 years
Pluto	3,660	248.4 years
Earth's Moon	239,000 miles from Earth	28 days

THE PLANETS ARE SHOWN IN SCALE
AGAINST A SEGMENT OF THE SUN

PERIOD OF ROTATION IN EARTH UNITS	DIAMETER IN MILES	MASS RELATIVE TO EARTH	DENSITY IN POUNDS PER CUBIC FOOT	SURFACE GRAVITY RELATIVE TO EARTH	SURFACE TEMPERATURE RANGE IN DEGREES F	PER CENT OF LIGHT REFLECTED
46 or 59 days	3,100	0.05	355	0.38	+750	0.06
247 days	7,700	0.81	322	0.89	+800	0.76
24 hours	7,927	1.00	344	1.00	−127/+136	0.39
24h 37m	4,200	0.10	243	0.38	−50/+ 90	0.15
9h 50m	88,800	317	81	2.54	−280/−200	0.51
10h 14m	75,100	95	45	1.2	−330/−240	0.50
10h 45m	31,000	14	100	1.07	−380/−270	0.66
15h 48m	28,000	17	138	1.4	−400/−330	0.62
6d 10h	3,600	0.8	200	0.7	−370	0.16
27d 7h 43m	2,160	0.012	208	0.165	−200/+200	0.07

INDEX